Abraham: *His Heritage and Ours*

Excavating the death pit at Ur of the Chaldees, the traditional city of Abraham's birth, where the joint expedition of the University of Pennsylvania Museum and the British Museum uncovered the royal pre-dynasic tombs of Ur, "probably the most important archaeological discovery of the century."

Abraham: *His Heritage and Ours*

By Dorothy B. Hill

Introduction by Sophia L. Fahs

BEACON PRESS   *Beacon Hill*   Boston

To

HELEN SEWELL

Artist
Author
Critic
Friend

IN MEMORIAM

Contents

List of Illustrations

Introduction

The portrait of Abraham, as presented in this book, is the result of a painstaking effort to remove the layers of legend and myth that have covered and blurred his picture and reveal the historical character who, most historians now believe, actually lived between 1,900 and 2,000 years before Christ. So far as we know it is a portrait never before shown outside the scholarly world. This narrative could not have been written thirty years ago. It is based not only upon an understanding of the records in Genesis, but also on the recently discovered, much older records that archaeologists have found in ancient mounds and caves scattered in various countries of the Middle East. To be sure, the narrative is still partly legendary, and it is influenced by the author's imagination, but this imagination is disciplined, and created by the patient putting together of many concrete items regarding the life and religions of the people of Abraham's world. These details have been gathered one by one from the artifacts and remains found in graves and cities buried under the dust of thousands of years, and from cuneiform writings on clay tablets, now translated and explained by men of learning. Furthermore, this book has been written with the personal help of several of the best of modern Biblical and archaeological scholars. Although the details included in any one episode can not be assuredly an accurate report of the historical event, yet these details are such as might have happened in the life of such a man as Abraham. Through her vivid writing, Mrs. Hill makes Abraham seem once again alive and real.

This book, however (as the author suggests), has a significance far beyond that of the life of one man — Abraham — for no man's life begins with his birth or ends with his death. To understand any historical character we need to know something about the generations before him with whose patterns of life and thought he began to weave his own web of life. Contrary to the traditional picture, Abraham is here presented, not as an illiterate, primitive nomad, but as the resident of one of the great cities of the ancient East. The author, therefore, rightly begins her story literally before the Flood, when Abraham's ancestors were migrating to the fertile valley between the Tigris and Euphrates rivers. Abraham is the heir of one of the first two great civilizations of which the world has as yet any written records. It was the Sumerians — among whom Abraham is said to have lived until manhood — from whom we have inherited, in revised form, our stories of *Creation, The Flood,* and *The Tower of Babel.* From the Sumerians came also, along with other important inventions, our sexagesimal system, our hour of sixty minutes and our day of twenty-four hours. Although not a Sumerian himself, Abraham (who was a Semite) lived in the midst of these people who had walled cities and well-built brick houses and great temples; whose kings and queens, over the years, had long known luxury; and whose goldsmiths' and gem-workers' products were "unsurpassed in ancient times and are second to none in all history." The religion of Sumer and Mesopotamia was the religion of Abraham's forebears and family. It was the religion of Abraham's youth. In manhood, the religion of the Canaanites surrounded him. Both religions deeply influenced his life, even though he was apparently one of those original personalities who achieved his own direct relations with the universe.

More than all this, here is the significant story of the beginnings of the modern world's three great religions — Judaism, Christianity, and Moslemism. All three faiths have called Abraham their spiritual father. All three have given him the unique title, "The Friend of God." His story should be of interest to the many million adherents of these three religions, at least to all those who care to understand how they came to believe and worship as they do.

The story of Abraham, as told in the Bible, can be found in Genesis, chapters 11 through 25. This narrative can be read in one short sitting. Books describing the archaeological discoveries of the life of peoples in Sumeria, Canaan, and Egypt during the second millennium B.C.E.* and earlier, with many fascinating illustrations — many more than could be included in this volume — can be found in public libraries and in specialized libraries of colleges, museums and theological seminaries. We hope that many of you may discover the thrill of exploring personally some of these recources.

Mrs. Hill's volume, however, will do what few readers can now do for themselves. It gathers the most significant facts out of both sources, the Bible and archaeology, and through their combination presents a vivid and interesting narrative that makes one feel imaginatively in the company of real people who lived, loved, fought, suffered and died some four thousand years ago.

SOPHIA L. FAHS

*B.C.E. stands for Beginning of the Common Era, a form which both Jews and Christians can use with ease.

Preface

This is more than the story of one man who, "in olden times," longed for a son to perpetuate his "name." Abraham's search for God and a homeland led him into the centers of three great civilizations. It is the story of that search and what lay behind and around it. It is Abraham and his son, *in situ.*

In situ is the term applied by archaeologists to the fixed position in which the treasures of their excavations are found and photographed before being removed from their original settings. *Abraham: His Heritage and Ours* is the story of Abraham, developed in its early setting, as revealed by archaeology.

This is more, then, than a legend treasured in the religious life of millions of Christians, Moslems, and Jews. For Abraham is more than a legend. He has become an historical figure, attested by the recent work of archaeologists and scholars. And this is true in spite of the fact that in no document *contemporary with his times* (late twentieth or early nineteenth century B.C.E.), as yet found, does the actual name of *Abraham, son of Terah,* appear. Nor is it likely to appear in the mass of excavated clay tablets, some legible, some fragmentary, that describe so well the life and peoples that surrounded him and shared his adventures.

From these tablets we discover that Abraham's migrations to Harran and Canaan were not isolated treks made by his family alone, but part of a general restlessness that, in his day, was beginning to stir the peoples of southwest Asia.

From recent excavations we reconstruct the history of ancient Mesopotamia, the "land between the rivers," Tigris and Euphrates, where Abraham grew to manhood. We discover the pattern and political history of its cities, the quality of its crafts, the beauty of its arts, the extent of its commerce, the growth and decline of its economy and, equally compelling, the importance of its gods and the impact of its religious concepts upon Abraham's beliefs. All this becomes evident because

xiii

now, in Iraq, archaeologists are digging into the barren mounds of earth that have long covered what was once a fruitful land of farms and pastures, dotted — as the mounds reveal — with busy, bustling Mesopotamian and Sumerian cities. Canaan, as well as Mesopotamia and Sumer, has been rediscovered; and excavations continue in Egypt.

The stories of the traditional Abraham are the basis of this book — Abraham's journeys to Harran, to Canaan, to Egypt; *The Battle of the Kings; Hagar and Ishmael; The Sacrifice of Isaac; The Destruction of Sodom and Gomorrah;* among others. They are interspersed with situations and characteristics that, while they are developed with imagination, are nonetheless based either upon factual archaeological discoveries or upon traditions of long standing.

The boy doubting the power of the images he was selling in the streets of Ur (chapter 6) is not necessarily the historical Abraham. He is an Abraham pictured by men of the early third century B.C.E. who looked upon such images quite differently from men of the nineteenth century B.C.E. and wished to present Abraham in the light of their own moral standards. Yet we know that, in Abraham's day, in all probability boys like Abraham did sell images in the streets of Sumer's cities, just as we have now discovered that they learned to read and write and cipher in the schoolhouses in whose ruins in Ur exercise tablets have been found.

The boy carrying his offering to the moon-god's temple in Ur (chapter 7) is not a record of the historical Abraham either, but we know from the excavations that in Abraham's time the temple and the ziggurat of Ur were there; thousands of clay receipt tablets were there, and there were clerks and boys and men; and one of the gift-bearers could have been Abraham.

Neither are the bandits on the road to Damascus (chapter 11) historic: their story is intended only to dramatize the dangers to which all travelers were liable on the treacherous roads between Mesopotamia and Canaan in that early day. And the petulance of the "beautiful," haughty, and capable Sarah (chapter 12) is only a characterization based on an oft repeated tradition regarding her.

On the other hand, other stories, such as *The Battle of the Kings* (chapter 19) and *The Destruction of Sodom and Gomorrah* (chapter 23), are, as they come from Genesis, historically and geographically consistent with our newer knowledge of Canaan. *The Battle of the Kings* demonstrates two points: the extent of trade which inspired such foreign rulers as the king of Elam to come all the way from the other side of the Tigris River to battle for access to the copper, gold, and manganese mines of Canaan; and the readiness and the need of the independent "princes" of Canaan to become "brothers-in-arms" in one another's behalf. Archaeology supports these points; and geology reappraises the story of Sodom and Gomorrah.

Quite different in content is the story of *The Huluppu Tree* (chapter 21) which is adapted from the translation of an authentic Sumerian myth (about 2000 B.C.E.) recorded on a clay tablet and dated almost contemporary with Abraham. It, too, demonstrates two points. It shows the whimsey, the nature-mindedness, and, at the same time, the intensity with which Mesopotamia's mother goddess was revered. It also shows — and this above all — how far we have been, and are, from understanding the significance of ancient religious concepts that were not at all whimsical to the Mesopotamians.

To archaeology also goes the credit in this book for the pre-Biblical versions of the stories of *Creation* and *The Flood* (chapters 3 and 4). These myths originated in the Mesopotamian valley and were recorded on the common clay tablets of the country.

Putting together the three sources — first, the Biblical story of Abraham from the Book of Genesis in the English Bible; then, for their picturesqueness, a few dramatic interpretations from the third century B.C.E.[28] *Book of Jubilees;* and, finally, and most important of all, material based upon authentic and illuminating discoveries of the past thirty years — putting together all these, I have tried to present the Abraham story in a setting consistent with the life of his times.

It is a pleasure to make grateful acknowledgment of the help I have had during the preparation of this book. To my friend Sophia Lyon Fahs, for her encouragement and enthusiasm; to the archaeologists and Biblical scholars Dr. William F. Albright of Johns Hopkins University and Dr. Robert H. Pfeiffer of Harvard University and to Dr. Angus H. MacLean of St. Lawrence University, each of whom read and approved the manuscript in its early stages; to Dr. Samuel N. Kramer, Curator of the Tablet Collection of the University of Pennsylvania Museum, for his permission to make use of his translation of the story of *the Huluppu Tree;* to Dr. Ernest W. Kuebler, Director of the Division of Education of the Council of Liberal Churches, and members of his curriculum committee for their criticisms; to Miss Helen Luitwieler, Librarian of the Andover Theological Library, Harvard; Miss E. Louise Lucas, Librarian of the Fogg Museum, Harvard; and Mrs. Caroline Dosker of the Photography Department of the University of Pennsylvania Museum; to Dr. William Stevenson Smith, Curator of the Department of Egyptian Art, Museum of Fine Arts, Boston; and to all the authors and publishers whose books and articles provided the research material the subject has required; and, lastly, to Mrs. Katharine Abt, who has shepherded the manuscript into print: my thanks.

DOROTHY B. HILL

Abraham: *His Heritage and Ours*

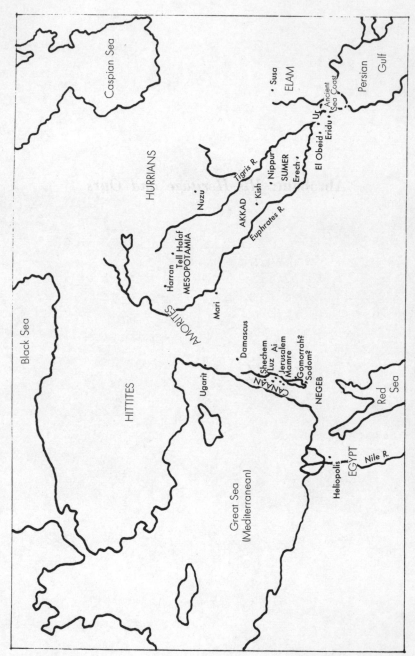

Ancient sites in Abraham's world (c. 1900 B.C.E.).

1
"Before Abraham Was . . ."

If centuries were hours and millennia only yesterdays, we could reach quickly into Abraham's era (about 1900 B.C.E.) and tell his story with a short perspective. Yet we must go back even farther than Abraham's day if we would understand the pattern of his life. For, contrary to the long-held belief in which Jews, Christians, and Moslems all portray their common ancestor as an illiterate nomad shepherd, it now seems evident that Abraham began his life in a land of sophisticated cities where men wrote and read and there were houses, schools, shops, and temples, and extensive commerce and industry.

The land had been called "the river country" in its earliest days for it was largely bounded by the great Tigris and Euphrates rivers, but later the north came to be known as *Mesopotamia* and *Akkad;* and the south as *Sumer.* Now, more often than not, the whole country, which is in the main our modern *Iraq,* is included in the Greek term, *Mesopotamia,* meaning "the land between the rivers," or in the general term, *Babylonia.*

The Mesopotamian-Sumerian civilization in which Abraham grew up was already old when Abraham was born (in fact, it is the oldest advanced civilization as yet known to scholars — even older than that of Egypt). In the thousand years before Abraham's time it had reached its peak and in his day was beginning to disintegrate. Who were these extraordinary people, the first of mankind — so far as scholars now know — to achieve a civilized pattern of life? And how did they achieve it? And what kind of life did their early efforts make possible for Abraham in the late twentieth or early nineteenth century B.C.E.?

To answer these questions, we must go back to a time when Abraham's ancestors, and ours, were roaming the moun-

3

tains and plains of southwest Asia or gathering into small settlements that grew into "cities" in this "land between the rivers."
For what these earliest peoples thought, and how they acted,
and the discoveries and inventions they made, as shown by
recent archaeological excavations, set the pattern for the new
picture of Abraham's life and thought, and color the whole
fabric of his story.[1]

In this country, as early as the fifth millennium (5000-
4000) B.C.E., primitive shepherds and hunters wrestled with the
urgent daily problem of keeping alive in a world that was mys-
tifying and frightening, and, at the same time, fascinating and
desirable. Safety, food, water, and some measure of comfort
and companionship — these were what our early ancestors
craved. In their search for them they encountered mysterious
powers that seemed to them to be hidden in things around them
— in trees, plants, stones, mountains, and in rivers and springs.
Their world was full of wonderful things they could not make.
Who, then, had made them?

They saw the food that grew out of the ground for their
nourishment cut down and blackened by frost. They saw the
sun overcome snow and ice and revitalize vegetation. They
watched springs of water bubble and "laugh" and defy them.
They saw plants bleed and die, as men could bleed and die.
There were mysterious forces whose powers they could not lo-
cate. These forces appeared to have life, spirit; just as each of
them had life and spirit. Men were buffeted by invisible winds,
burnt by fire, pelted by rain, and overwhelmed by floods. They
could not control the forces that surrounded them.

Living under many obscurities, was it strange that
early man should conclude that there was another world around
him, full of invisible life — a world that acted independently
of him, peopled by unseen spirits; in other words, a *spiritual*
world?

To him it seemed quite as important to keep on good terms
with this hidden world as with his neighbors. To draw himself
into the good graces of its invisible inhabitants, lest in anger
they turn against him, appeared to him imperative. His problem was how to placate such spirits. If only he could find a way

to do this! Surely there was some formula of address, some little ritual, some dramatic act that would please the spirits so much that they would favor him and his family; or that would, at least, turn away the wrath of those that might, otherwise, have become unfriendly to him. But where was he to find it?

Fear and hope alternated constantly in his mind. He was ready to try, over and over again, any ritual that had ever seemed to influence anyone's "luck." And he would continue that ritual, hopefully, year after year, and pass it on to his children, regardless of his own success with it.

He would mold a tiny clay figure of his enemy, stab it with holes, and then bury or burn it, hoping he had killed his enemy; but, alas, the man went right on living and, like as not, continued to annoy him for many a year. On rocks and on the walls of caves, he would scratch the outline of a fish he hoped to catch, or paint a spear clear through the painted body of a stag he hoped to kill; still he might come home with a turtle and a rabbit!

He would drain blood into the ground and cover it, thinking thereby to appease the angry spirit of a murdered man. He would mumble a ritual over a bulbous blob of clay, praying for both the fertility of his people and the fertility of his fields. Death (which he feared above all experiences) he was never able to overcome in spite of his efforts; but he kept right on with the ritual of sprinkling red ochre over the corpse, hoping that the color, the life, would return to the pale, dead body. There was no end to the fantastic formulas he was willing to repeat.

There was, however, a natural force — visible, predictable and mysterious — from which Abraham's ancestors drew great comfort. That was the moon. Whether these men lived in the shadow of the mountains in the north where the two rivers had their rise, or in the stillness of the plains to the south where the rivers nearly met on their way to the Persian Gulf, night after night, they followed the moon's course as it rose and slowly lighted the dark earth.

Born a pale little crescent in the afternoon sky, they saw it develop each night a rounder, sturdier body, until at last the ruddy, full moon rode high above them. Then, gradually, old age overcame the moon, just as age weakened a man. Night by night, it appeared to shrink, becoming smaller, paler, weaker, as the end approached. Finally, a night came when it failed to rise at all. And another night and another. But the moon was not forever dead and gone, the people said, because on the third day it rose again, reborn. Then all was well. And the life cycle repeated itself. It had always been like that, the old folk said. People learned when to expect the moon's comings and its goings. They could depend upon it.

Men looked to the moon to light the path of their journeys, for they often traveled by night. They looked to the moon for "light" to solve their problems: only to walk under its pale light calmed a man's fears and brought him peace and fresh courage.

Abraham's ancestors reverenced the moon. They believed it was immortal. They were "uplifted" by its presence and, again and again, they called upon the moon to "show the way." They yearned to become a part of such great power as it possessed, in order always to be able in life "to see where they were going," and, like the moon, to be born again after death.

They were hunters and shepherds — and some became primitive farmers as well — these early peoples who roamed "the river country" and looked to the moon for guidance. In their search for security, they turned, not only to the moon, but to other forces of Nature whose powers they recognized but little understood. They longed to be strong like the wind, fruitful like the earth, secure like the rock, creative like the sun, and like the moon to have everlasting life.

But their experience was limited. They were shepherds. Because they knew their sheep and called each one by name and every sheep knew its shepherd, they concluded that the mysterious, invisible power that seemed to overshadow their lives was a shepherd also, and that they and their wives and little ones were his sheep. The sun on their backs in the morning as they led their own sheep to pasturage was the hand of the invisible shepherd directing their day. The moon that lighted their path at night was the firebrand by which this good shepherd, who knew their needs and problems, led them to food and water and safety. The people of "the river country" called this mysterious, invisible power *An* or *Anu* (literally, "high"). An was their shepherd, and they were "the flocks of An." It was as simple as that in the beginning.

To other invisible powers, also, they gave names and personalities. The force of the storm was *Enlil;* of the earth, *Enki;* of the water, *Ea;* and *Inanna* was the great, creative mother, "the mistress of heaven." It was these invisible forces, these mysterious *gods,* they said, who had created mankind, in order that man might honor the gods and labor on earth for them. Men thought of the unseen forces as living together on some invisible height, building homes, working, loving, even quarreling, quite as simply as they themselves built their homes and labored and loved and contended on earth. There was nothing menial in labor, then, for gods or men. But the whims of the gods were difficult to foresee.

In earliest times, everyone had stood in the same relation to the spirit world. All were equally vulnerable. All were fearful. But as soon as it was noised about that one man had been more than ordinarily successful in appearing to placate some invisible force or to forecast some disaster or success, he was "looked up to" in his community.

Other men flocked to him, only too willing to pay for his "wisdom" and advice with foodstuffs and labor. The "gifted one" was able to withdraw from the work performed by his neighbors. He lived a comfortable, profitable life: hunters, shepherds and farmers gladly supported him. Thus there developed, in time, a unique group of respected men whose living came from other men's labor.

As centuries passed, the early Mesopotamian learned to make whatever he needed by way of weapons and tools and utensils. What he made, he named; and the name endued it with life. He believed that just as he and his family — and even his sheep and goats — had personalities and could be called by name and just as the invisible powers had names and personalities, so had the familiar objects around him. He would call upon his weapons and tools and all his handicraft, upon Nature, and upon his foodstuffs, as personally as one would address a man. In his myths, recorded in later years, such conversations have come to light.

In honeyed tones he would beg the arrow to find its mark; with stern upbraidings he would berate it when it missed. He had words of praise for the seeds that sprouted, and stinging reproaches for the dull sickle that failed to cut the grain.

"O, Bow, . . .," "O, Grain, . . .," "O, Salt, . . .," "O, Fire, . . .," he would say, "do thus and so for me"; or, in anger, ". . . why have you done this thing to me?" [2]

With the invention of a rude plough and the first uses of oxen, the people of "the river country" were able more easily to raise their food supplies. They learned, too, to dig canals to expand and irrigate the land.

They learned to make pots out of the Mesopotamian clay, and decorated them. In time, they learned to fire their pottery and even to glaze it so that their pitchers and jars and pots would hold liquids.

They learned to make mud bricks, at first by hand, sun-dried; and later in molds; and, finally, to fire them, also. Their knowledge of the uses of fire and the art of fire-making brought about the "magical" discovery of what heat could do to certain ores and silicates, and later led to the production and use of bronze.

The early Mesopotamians learned to spin yarn from the wool of their sheep and to make thread from the fibers of the flax plant. On looms of their own invention, they wove woolen and linen cloth. However, through the years, the sheepskin skirt long continued to be their commonest article of clothing.

When they converted a shell into a hide scraper, a flint into a knife or a jaw bone into a sickle, clay into a jar or wool into a blanket, these people felt they were creators. They could not comprehend by what "magic" they were able to strike and control fire. Nor did they understand how the liquid copper, which they poured from the heated rock into molds of varying design, hardened into an axe-head or an image at their "command." But in all these acts, each man felt that he had gained some little control over a natural, invisible force.

That some men in a community should excell others in manual skill was inevitable. Out of this situation there de-

veloped, in time, side by side with the "gifted ones," another
special group of men. These were the artisans — the pot-
makers and weavers, the metal-workers and basket-makers, the
men who built houses and barns and the earliest temples.
Among the artisans were raft- and boat-builders and sledge-
and cart-makers whose handiwork made it possible to transport
home-grown products and the work of local craftsmen to ever-
expanding markets.

It was the discovery of the principle of the wheel that made
some of these expansions possible. Use of the potter's wheel
also increased the ceramic output, although for many centuries
some of the most beautiful bowls and jars continued to be made
by the old, built-up, hand process.

During this early period, many different tribes wandered
into the fertile valleys between the two rivers, spreading their
tents and adobe huts over the land. They came from the shores
of the Black and Caspian seas, from the mountains to the north
and east of Mesopotamia, and from the desert to the west.

Although these people came from a number of different
directions and spoke different dialects, largely their languages
had a common root. Most of the dialects were Semitic. The
Semites settled, in those earliest years, in what is now the
northern half of "the land between the rivers," for in those days
the Persian Gulf reached as much as a hundred miles farther
north than now and the southern portion of the valley was
largely marshland.

In the spring when the ice and snows in the Armenian
Mountains melted, the two great rivers flooded their banks.
The danger of serious floods in the north was not as great as
in the south where the plains through which their mighty
waters rushed were unbelievably flat and low. The overflowing
rivers fanned out as they neared the gulf and the flood waters,
with the fertile silt they contained, spread over many miles of
territory.

Thick clouds of fog rose from these steamy marshlands.
Then slowly, day after day, year after year, the sun cut through
the mist. As the fog lifted and the mud dried, little islands of
fertile land appeared where vegetation became lush and where

game and wild fowl nested and fed. Many muddy puddles lay
dotted over the plains. The deeper ones became brackish pools
in which fish thrived and marsh reeds grew.

On small patches of land, here and there, a few adventurous families built their crude settlements in the south. A
picture and story of the life of any of these earliest villages can
be pieced together today from some of the light green, hand-
painted pottery and crude flint tools and traces of plaited reed
mats discovered at *el Obeid*. Such evidence was found in an ex-
cavation that reached the very floor of the original delta and
it represents the earliest clearly defined culture of the country.[3] But it was not the Obeidians, or any of the Semitic tribes-
men, who were destined to develop this land. It was the vigor
and genius and art — together with the skilled leadership and
amazing cooperative effort — of a group of foreigners who
peacefully invaded the valley some time before 3500 B.C.E. and,
side by side with the northern Mesopotamians, created the
great Sumerian civilization.

2

The Amazing Sumerians

Considerable mystery still hides the origin of the Sumerians. At some early time — during the Obeidian age in Mesopotamia — these non-Semitic people, speaking a language new to "the river country," migrated to the southern marshes of "the land between the rivers." Their appearance, as well as their language, was strikingly different from the Semites'. Proud of their heavy, glossy, black hair, they called themselves "the black-headed ones." But who they were and just where they came from, no one actually knows.

In their traditions there were stories of mountain life. They were familiar also with rivers and seas, for they came knowing how to build rafts and navigate rivers, and with some experience in artificial irrigation. Some scholars think they migrated from as far as the Indus valley or from the Zagros Mountains or from regions bordering Lake Van or the Caspian Sea.

The Sumerians were a gifted people. They came into the Euphrates valley already equipped with a knowledge of basketry and pottery making and of spinning and weaving, and already skilled in agriculture and in the breeding of sheep and goats. They were familiar with metalworking and had learned to combine copper and tin to make bronze. Their art shows that they had four-wheeled wooden wagons and two-wheeled chariots drawn by some kind of small animal that looked somewhat like a small wild horse and somewhat like an ass.[4]

Above all, whatever their origin, the Sumerians were a people not afraid of hard work, for it was no child's play to drain the marshes that covered the delta of the Tigris and Euphrates rivers. In this flat, muddy, tree-less, stone-less land that we should have called most unpromising, the newcomers went to work with all the eagerness and enthusiasm of pioneers.

They cut swaths in the marsh reeds to make floor spaces

11

A Sumerian dignitary. Not always were "the black-headed" pictured with flowing locks; they were often pictured shaven and shorn.

for their houses; they tied live reeds in bunches to make posts for the side walls; they tied the tips of these bunches together overhead to make the roof beams. Then they hung mats woven of plaited reeds between and over the living reed posts and plastered the mats with mud. And that was only the beginning of their labors.

In a country where floods forever threatened not only their homes and crops but their very lives, they dug canals. Through bundles of reinforcing reeds laid end to end on the sides of these canals, they strained the muddy waters until only the sediment remained; and the mud, when it dried, made dykes and sea walls to restrain and direct the waters.

At long, long last their efforts were rewarded. Ever-widening areas of dry land appeared — a fruitful land, crossed and crisscrossed by irrigation canals that made channels of communication between settlements. Lush fields of barley and wheat spread over the flat lands around the villages and provided the ingredients for an abundance of bread and beer. There was pasturage now for sheep and goats and cattle; and men began to experiment with the cultivation of fruits and vegetables. And the artisans went back to their crafts.

For a thousand years Sumerian influence spread and mingled with the Semitic. The gods and myths of one became the gods and myths of the other. In industry also, not so much one people or the other alone, but side by side, they achieved the discoveries and inventions historians credit to these early years in "the river country." The Sumerians were more skilful as farmers and craftsmen than the Semites. Soon their output tended to outstrip that of the older inhabitants.

As the rate of food production increased through better cultivation, there was a surplus of food and a surplus of beer to store and barter. For this the craftsmen had already devised both the glazed and the unglazed jar.

Storing his foodstuffs in jars, a man needed some means of identification, some badge of ownership, which would keep his products from being used or claimed by his neighbor. For this, he learned to make small, stone-like cylinders, each inscribed with its owner's special mark of identification. When such cylinders were rolled over the soft clay of a jar in the making, or over its stopper, it put his seal upon the jar or stopper, irrevocably. What was marked by it was one man's possession, his good fortune to own — his *mannu.* To all others it was "Don't touch!" — *taboo,* ill fortune.[5]

Men came to believe that the seal possessed magical properties to guard the possession it adorned and to influence its owner's good fortune by means of his touching it. Sometimes he hung a blob of clay marked with his special symbol around the neck of his jar; sometimes he hung it, like a bead, around his own neck for a "charm." Thus, the cylinder seal became both a mark of identification and an amulet.

In time, the craftsmen of Mesopotamia and Sumer increased their output sufficiently to supply both their local needs and an export market. Artisans joined traders' caravans and visited distant settlements where they learned new techniques and discovered new materials.

In proportion to the success of their foreign trading, the wealth at home increased. Men were able to barter for more costly materials, such as gold, silver, copper, lapis lazuli, and malachite, to use in place of local clay, obsidian, shell, and bone. As their businesses prospered, the artisans were able, and willing, to pay "the gifted ones" substantial fees for special services, and to build homes for them.

Gradually, "the gifted ones" developed formal rituals for the services they sold to the people. Years passed. The rituals grew longer and more secret, the rewards larger and more frequent, and more and more men apprenticed themselves to that group of honored advisers.

Early man *needed* his "gifted ones" and his soothsayers: to the extent their advice was able to dispel his fears, they were a healthful necessity. The usefulness of these men continued to increase until out of their services there evolved, in time, the office of *priest* — a unique and highly "reverenced" adviser, protector and leader, set apart by the nature of his services to minister to and satisfy the needs and problems of his supporters.

What these men meant to their communities was far more than our imagination can picture. Now the Mesopotamian and Sumerian had someone to stand between him and the unseen forces he feared. Let Enlil blow his wildest blast of wind and blacken the earth with his darkest storm clouds! Let Ea unleash all the waters of the earth! Let the sun overpower (eclipse) the moon! Man was not alone: he had someone to plead for him. The people of "the river country" were still "the flocks of An," but now the priests were An's shepherds, the custodians of An's flocks.

Settlements grew. Trade increased. Profits accrued. The services of the priests expanded. And soon the largest accumulation of weath in a community was building up in the hands of the priests. Not only did they grow rich in their own rights, but they became custodians of everything early man donated to the spirit powers. But such a situation did not seem unreasonable to the Semites and Sumerians. They assumed that the gods had always had a prior claim upon the land and its bounties and that they, An's people, were at best no more than tenants by the gods' grace. Even the most honored priest called himself the gods' "tenant farmer."

When towns grew and the complexities of community life demanded that some strong, central government be established, the people turned naturally to the priests. Someone had to decide who might harvest a field and how much water from the neighboring canal a farmer might claim. For many years the Mesopotamians had been accustomed to the thought that the priests were the men to settle their differences. Now it seemed fitting that the priests should oversee all phases of their lives.

The priests doled out to the people parcels of farmland, seeds, and even ploughs and sickles. They set apart an area in each city sacred to their own use and designated certain other land as common pasturage for the community. And the people returned "rents" and fees to the gods through the gods' priestly custodians.

The priests were not long satisfied with the modest shelters provided as the gods' first earthly homes. They told their people that "in dreams" a god had "directed" them to build or rebuild the god's earthly dwelling, saying that the god had even designated the size and alignment of the temple; but it was the priests, of course, who planned it. To such divine commands, the artisans responded with materials and labor, the farmers brought food for the workmen, and the bakers and brewers provided bread and beer.

Sacred areas were increased in size and temples made larger, but the site of the god's house, once it had been established, rarely changed except to grow bigger. Each temple was built upon the remains of its predecessor, just as each village periodically rose to a new level on the fallen house-walls of the last. Thus there accumulated, over many centuries, layer upon layer of rubble. And in this rubble, layer by layer, lay the remains of pottery, weapons, utensils, and tools which had been made and used by the people or brought to the temple as gifts and fees, or even manufactured in the temple's own workshops.

Because these ancient artifacts have lain largely undisturbed, the layers are relatively distinct. By comparing the types and decorations and materials of objects found in one layer at one site with those found at another site, archaeologists are able *to date both the artifacts and the settlements.*

Excavations show that as the early settlements of Mesopotamia and Sumer grew into villages and the villages into cities, the priests became an organized body of administrators, responsible for all phases of their communities' daily life, for the maintenance of irrigation canals and flood walls, for the defense of the land; and in touch with similar administrators in neighboring cities.

Now, the priests needed some method of recording their business transactions. It was not enough for one priest to remember that he had received so much wool from such and such a shepherd and assigned it to a certain weaver; or how much grain had been collected in rents and placed in the temple's storage bins; or how many pack animals and how many baskets of dates had been supplied a certain trader going north; or how many oxen the priest had promised to send as a New Year's offering to Enlil's temple in Nippur. Some record, distinguishable to the local priests and, in time, to neighboring priesthoods as well, must be devised.[6]

Out of this need the Sumerians evolved the art of writing. The earliest, numerical scratches developed into cuneiform

Archaic pictographic writing on stone.

characters, neatly dug into a soft clay tablet by a sharp-ended stylus and hardened into place by baking the tablet.

To the original symbols for recording measurements and receipts was later added a wider and more complicated vocabulary until, its use spreading from one city to another, this early cuneiform alphabet became general in all "the land between the rivers."

That the invention of the first alphabet was definitely the product of the genius of the Sumerians is evidenced by the fact that the language used was the Sumerian tongue, and not the Semitic. For two thousand years, even after the Semitic Akkadian had become the common language and the Sumerian was no longer spoken by the people generally, Sumerian still

Writing in cuneiform on soft clay tablet.

remained the classical language throughout the entire Middle East.[7]

With the invention of writing (some time before 3000 B.C.E.), human history is said to begin. One by one, in "the river country," man's early needs had been satisfied by his inventions and discoveries,[8] all of them important; but the art of writing, with the many records of social organization, history, mythology, and literature it provided, was perhaps the Sumerians' major contribution.

This gifted people had immigrated to a land already occupied by another people. They had cooperated in a common life and absorbed the best in the Semitic culture; and soon, because of an acknowledged superiority, they had dominated the culture. They made valuable, basic contributions to mankind and left an indelible mark upon the whole history of civilization. Yet our grandfathers could not so much as have asked the question: *Which of the languages — Semitic or Sumerian — did Abraham learn to speak as a child?* because, until some thirty years ago, not even the most learned of Biblical scholars had ever heard of such a people as the Sumerians. Nor could they have known that a thousand years before Abraham was born people were learning to write and read and cipher.

It is these records, written on clay tablets in cuneiform, which archaeologists now excavate and translate and offer as evidence (along with the tools and utensils and pottery of the people), that provide a more authentic and less legendary background for Abraham's story.

3

Who Created the World?

When, after many generations had passed, people began to ask: *Who created the world?*, the Sumerians were not at a loss for an answer. They knew how the world had come to be — at least *their* world, Sumer. From tales their ancestors had handed down to them and from clay tablets that recorded the tradition, they pictured the steps by which it had been created. And when, centuries later, Sumer faded into obscurity and her clay tablets were buried and forgotten in the debris that covered the land, still the Sumerian legend persisted, carried from one country to another in various forms, one of which became the first chapter of the English Bible.

At first, mist, fog, "chaos," had covered everything, the Sumerians said. Then some powerful force (the sun) cut through the fog and lifted the steamy mist from the marshes, revealing the sky and dividing the sky from the waters under the sky. When (through draining the marshes) the waters under heaven were gathered together in one place, dry land appeared. The dry land was Earth, they said, and the gathering together of the water was Seas.

The earth put forth grass, and herb yielding seed after his kind, and the tree yielding fruit, whose seed was in itself. . . . And for signs (for planting) and for seasons (for harvesting) and for days of the year, there were lights in the firmament of heaven, the greater light to rule the day and the lesser light to rule the night; and stars also.

Then the waters brought forth abundantly every moving creature that had life; and birds began to fly above the earth in the open firmament of heaven. Fish multiplied in the waters of the seas; and birds multiplied on the earth. The earth brought forth every living creature after its kind, cattle and

20

creeping things, insects, and wild beasts of the earth after their kind.

Having subdued the marshlands, man multiplied to populate this new land where his food was provided by "every herb bearing seed and every tree whose seed was in itself." In his new home, man had "dominion over the fish of the sea, and over the fowl of the air, and over the cattle, and over all the earth [agriculture] . . . and over every living thing that moveth upon the earth."

The early settlers knew, and told their children, how the world — *their world* — had been created. They knew each successive step in the process. Who but the Sumerians had dug the mud and hauled the sledges? Who but they had built the walls? It was the Sumerians who had known the long, grueling, exhaustive labor it had required. Who else had submitted to laws and regulations laid down in the interests of their common goal? Had not their very homes, their huts of plaited straw, hung between water and land, crowded to the extreme edge of every expanding piece of ground in order that a maximum of food for the workmen might be raised within its borders? Who but the Sumerians had endured the hardships?

But when the work was finished and the Sumerians looked out over their network of canals and upon the fertility of their fields, they were awed by the magnitude of their success. Was it *they*, after all, who had done this wonderful thing?

They asked themselves: who of us made out the plan, inspired the labor? Who of us created the wild grasses and the palm tree sprouts? Who of us supplied the game and birds and cattle, hung lights in the sky and filled the seas with fish? They knew that no one of them alone could have conceived, let alone brought to fruition, such bounty as the plain provided — such crops of grain and vegetables and fruit, such pasturage. Except the evidence lay spread before their eyes, it were a dream.

The reverence and awe with which their ancestors had regarded the mysterious natural forces of the world impressed them now. They, too, were An's people, and their priests were the gods' shepherds. Perhaps, after all, they said, it was some

invisible "god on high" who had created the world and Sumer's
earliest settlers had been but the tools, the instruments, in the
gods' service.

These people believed that the gods' purpose in creating
"the black-headed" (the Sumerians) had been three-fold: in
order that man might establish shrines for the gods' worship;
in order that man might labor in the gods' fields; and in order
that there be someone to offer "sweet-savored sacrifices" for
the gods' nourishment. The early Sumerians strove to satisfy
these demands. Had they been living in their original homeland, perhaps they would have climbed the mountains to meet
their "god on high."

Here in Sumer, there were no mountains; only mud.

"Out of the mud, let us mold bricks," they said, "and bind
them together with bitumen, and build a man-made mountain,
a staircase of bricks over which An can descend to dwell among
us."

Another long concentration of labor followed. At the Sumerian settlement of *Erech* (Uruk, Warka) on the Euphrates
River, they built a mound from hand-formed lumps of mud —
thirty-five feet high it was, with one house for the god on its
flattened top and another at its base.

In time, they duplicated the mound which they had made
at Erech in half a dozen other settlements that grew up along
the river and canals. Then the Sumerians went on with their
cattle raising and farming, their hunting and fishing and
shepherding, their crafting and trading and building and wor-
shiping, in this new and fruitful land which was peculiarly their
own. And now they declared it was the gods on high who
had created the world and built their cities — Eridu, Erech, Ur,
Lagash, Kish . . . — and left a special god to reign over each
city.

In their literature they described, and in their art they
pictured, a creation of heaven as well as earth. The gods then
dug canals. The gods made bunches of heavenly reeds and
laid them, end to end, along the banks. The gods strained
watery mud through reinforcing reeds to make the flood walls
and drain the fields. It was the only way the Sumerians knew
of creating a homeland.

A Sumerian tablet recording the stories of The Creation, The Flood, and The Fall of Man.

A cuneiform tablet with envelope (time of Abraham).

Later Sumerians (Babylonians) presented *their* story of Creation. It, too, was a mythical record of their ancestors' labors and the steps by which the land of Sumer had come into being some time before 3500 B.C.E. In one form or another, the story survives to the present day. One version is a Semitic poem glorifying *Marduk*, the Babylonians' sun-god-king, who, after a gory struggle, overcomes the forces of *Tiamat*, the "chaos" goddess, out of whose body he creates both heaven and earth.[9] It was written in cuneiform on seven clay tablets, as early, probably, as about 2500 B.C.E.[10]

We of today wonder in what form Abraham first heard the Sumerian story of *Creation*. We wonder, too, who could have put into writing, many centuries later, the Biblical version that has come down to us. Memories of ancestral experiences, bequeathed from generation to generation, seem to breathe through its lines. And we can only conclude that in later years some devout worshiper, awed as the Sumerians had been by the endless mystery of Creation, refined the thoughts of these ancient people and distilled from them the poetic beauty and dignity of the first chapter of Genesis.

In the beginning God created the heaven and the earth.

And the earth was waste and void; and darkness was upon the face of the deep; and the Spirit of God moved upon the face of the waters.

And God said, Let there be light; and there was light.

And God saw the light, that it was good; and God divided the light from the darkness.

And God called the light Day, and the darkness he called Night. And there was evening and there was morning, one day. . . .

And God made the firmament, and divided the waters which were under the firmament from the waters which were above the firmament: . . .

.   .   .   .

And God said, Let the waters under the heavens be gathered together into one place, and let the dry land appear: and it was so.

And God called the dry land Earth: and the gathering together of the waters called he Seas: and God saw that it was good.

And God said, Let the earth put forth grass, and herbs yielding seed, and fruit-trees bearing fruit after their kind, wherein is the seed thereof, upon the earth: and it was so.

And the earth brought forth grass, and herbs yielding seed after their kind, and trees bearing fruit, wherein is the seed thereof, after their kind: and God saw that it was good, . . .

.   .   .   .

And God said, Let the waters swarm with swarms of living creatures, and let birds fly above the earth in the open firmament of heaven.

And God created the great sea monsters, and every living creature that moveth, wherewith the waters swarmed, after their kind, and every winged bird after its kind: and God saw that it was good.

.   .   .   .

And God created man in his own image, in the image of God created he him; male and female created he them.

And God blessed them; and God said unto them, Be fruitful, and multiply, and replenish the earth, and subdue it: and have domination over the fish of the sea, and over the birds of the heavens, and over every living thing that moveth upon the earth.

And God said, Behold, I have given you every herb bearing seed, which is upon the face of all the earth, and every tree in which is the fruit of the tree yielding seed; to you it shall be for meat.

.   .   .   .

And God saw everything he had made, and, behold, it was very good. . . .[11]

4

The Great Flood—in Legend and in Fact

Suppose you were excavating the site of an ancient Sumerian city. You are in the process of digging an exploratory shaft from top to bottom of the mound to uncover, layer by layer, the successive cities that may have been built on the site since earliest times. You have reached a level, let us say, that from the style of its pottery remains can be dated about 2500 B.C.E. Still, you are not content, since, even yet, the workmen are finding occasional tools and potsherds (broken pottery) and other objects of interest.

Suddenly the type of pottery changes: its colors and design become more consistent. Mostly it is dark-colored, red combined with yellow and black decorations. You know archaeologists have named that particular style of pottery for the location at which it was first discovered and that, by and large, it was the common pottery of the country at a certain period.

"*Jemdet Nasr* ware; about 3000 B.C.E.!" you exclaim and continue the digging.

After a little, the quality of both the pottery's material and its workmanship appears to improve. There is freshness and vigor in both design and execution. Some of the pottery is black or grey, but most of it is red. It is unpainted and highly polished. There is evidence it was made on a potter's wheel, then baked and made smoky in a kiln. Pottery such as this was first found in excavating the Sumerian city of Erech (Warka).

"*Warkan* ware; fourth millennium!" you observe with pride.

The digging goes on, each level's "finds" being older than the last. Finally, a more primitive type of pottery appears: pale greenish or pinkish in color, with painted decorations in black or brown. You recognize it as *Obeidian* ware; and this would have been contemporary to the earliest days of Sumerian occupation. Will the next level reveal any evidence of the

26

exquisite, thin, smooth, polychrome painted *Halafian* pottery, a type first found at the northern Mesopotamian site of *Tell Halaf;* or was Halafian ware even older than the Sumerians' reclamation of the marshlands? There is no need to ask, for the "finds" have ceased.

Now the men are digging in what they call "clean clay": no pottery, no utensils, no weapons, no debris of any sort. The workmen think they have come to the floor of the original delta, but measurements show this is not the case.[12] Two feet, four, six, the digging continues through the clean clay. At a depth of eight feet the clean clay deposit stops and the diggers come upon a new layer of rubbish, strewn with shards of early Obeidian pottery. Primitive tools made of flint and bone appear. There is evidence of dried marsh slime and even imprints of plaited reed mats wherever a bowl has covered the matting. Now you have indeed reached the floor of the delta and found remains of one of its first, primitive settlements. You are close to 4000 B.C.E.

Your imaginative "dig" has been over-simplified: actually, artifacts would rarely lie in quite such perfect strata. But if all this had been your good fortune to discover, you could have been sure, as was Sir Leonard Woolley as he appraised the eight foot deposit of clean clay below his own excavations of a cemetery at Ur, that in Sumer some time in the Obeidian period of culture a tremendous flood had devastated the land.[13]

Can you imagine the excitement and satisfactions of such a find! Sir Leonard recalled the Flood story in the Old Testament: how God, because of the wickedness of men, sent a mighty deluge to destroy all mankind, except only the pious Noah and his family and enough animals and birds to replenish the earth once the devastation was complete.

He recalled, too, and with added excitement no doubt, certain clay tablets that had already been found elsewhere in Mesopotamia: one, a fantastic myth of the destruction of "the world" by flood; and others on which were inscribed, in cuneiform, lists of *"kings before . . ."* and *"kings after the Flood."*[14] Could this discovery be anything but the result of the deluge described in Genesis? he asked, and were the lists a record of historical, not mythical, kings, after all? It was one of the most exciting moments in the history of archaeology.

In its early Sumerian versions the Flood story is primitive and polytheistic.

Ziusudra or *Utnaphishtim* — call him by his early Sumerian or by his later Babylonian name — was "the wise one," for wisdom was ever the crowning attribute of mythological heroes. Again and again, it is "the wise one" among the gods who creates a situation, or a "wise" mortal who hears the god's admonitions and responds with gifts and sacrifices.

Ziusudra (meaning "Life's Day Prolonged"), or Utnaphishtim ("Day of Life"), was a mortal looking for the secret of immortality. Many centuries had passed since primitive men first watched the mysterious moon wane and die and "rise again, new born," but no one had yet uncovered the secret of rebirth.[15] To find the key to the doors of life-everlasting was, for the Sumerians, their heroes' most popular objective.

According to the legend, Ziusudra, "the wise mortal," is a pious priest. He lives in a reed hut, its walls plastered with mud, in true Sumerian style.

Now the gods meet in assembly. There is *Anu* (An), god of heaven; *Enlil,* of wind and storm; *Enki,* of the earth; and *Ea,* god of the watery abyss. And there is *Ninhursag* (Inanna), "the lady potter," "the builder of that which has breath." With her help, the gods have created from clay "the black-headed" (the Sumerians), in order "that the services of the gods may be established and that their shrines may be built." However, "the black-headed" have become negligent in their duties and, in anger, the assembly of the gods votes to destroy mankind. Meanwhile Inanna, goddess of heaven, "the ever-wailing maid," wails loudly in protest over the destruction of "her people"; but to no avail.

Then Enki decides secretly to warn Ziusudra, the pious priest. He enlists Ea's help, since it is Ea, in Sumerian mythology, who is generally given the task of carrying out the other gods' decisions. Sumerian gods do not speak directly to their people, but only through a dream or an emissary, often a priest; but in this case, the gods speak through *a wall.* After the

assembly has voted to destroy mankind, "Ea, the lord of wisdom . . . to the reed hut proclaims these words: 'Reed hut,
hear; house wall, give heed . . . by our hand a flood . . . ' "
he warns the priest. In his hut, Ziusudra, the pious priest, the
mortal man, listens intently. He receives the god's secret warning through the good offices of the wall. Fearfully, each day
he prostrates himself before a sacred wooden image he has
made. Then, at Ea's advice, Ziusudra builds a square boat or
box in which to save himself, his family, and all that is his.

A terrible storm ensues, so terrible that the gods themselves
weep and, in their fear, "crouch like dogs against the walls of
heaven." When the storm is over, Ziusudra lets in the light of
the sun-god through an opening he makes in the side of his
ship. He lets out a dove, but the dove returns having found
no place to perch. He lets out a swallow, but the swallow too
comes back. He lets out a raven, and the raven flies free, for
now the waters are subsiding. The boat rests upon land.

Ziusudra opens the door and finds that "all the world" is
devastated and all the people of the earth have been turned
back into clay!

Presently, the gods discover that "the seed of mankind"
has not been totally destroyed after all, for Ziusudra still lives;
and Enki is blamed for having allowed any member of the
human race to survive. But the pious priest bows down to the
sun-god who has brought back light and warmth to the earth.
He "sacrifices an ox, a sheep he slaughters, . . . before Anu
and Enlil [heaven and earth] he bows himself down."

The gods repent. They decide to make the pious Ziusudra
one of them (perhaps because, unwittingly, Ziusudra has saved
the sources of their sweet-savored sacrifices and the worshipers
upon whom the gods' shrines depend). "Eternal life like that
of a god," Enki gives to him; "an eternal soul like that of a god
he creates for him." *Ziusudra has found immortality.* And
afar off, at the mouth of the rivers, the gods give Ziusudra, the
wise and pious priest, and his family a land in which to dwell.[16]

Such was an early version of the popular Deluge myth
which the Mesopotamians carried to the north and west and
which, through a later (Babylonian) version, finally came down

to us, much refined and no longer polytheistic, as the Biblical story of Noah, his ark, and the Flood.[17]

Flood stories encircle the world. Wherever rivers rise and overflow their banks disastrously, they appear. Egypt is the exception, since the Nile River inundations are predictable, restrainable, and beneficial. "The myth of the Great Flood appears among the oldest religious inheritances of mankind," writes Dr. Albright. Such stories go back to the last Ice Age when, without doubt, the melting torrents of retreating ice overwhelmed vast regions of North America, Europe, and Asia.[18]

In excavating a number of Sumer's other cities, archaeologists have found, between layers of interrupted cultures, other deposits of flood silt of such spectacular depth as to suggest a deluge of catastrophic size, even in a country where flood deposits are not uncommon. Such evidence and additional flood stories come from the cities of Shuruppak and Kish. The various versions of the legend meet and mingle. But the hero is always the wise man, the friend of the god, who builds a boat at the god's command and saves his pious family from annihilation and a wicked world from complete depopulation.

Not all the world, or even all the Sumerians' "world," was destroyed by flood, however; nor was mankind obliterated. In those days of limited communication even prodigious floods were more local than the Sumerians supposed. Nonetheless, some time before 3000 B.C.E., some one deluge in this country was an overpowering and widespread calamity.

This was the flood, presumably, that cut Sumer's early history in two, chronologically, and inspired the lists of "kings before . . ." and "kings after the Flood." And this was the deluge referred to on clay tablets that tell us: "After the flood, kingship returned to the earth" and "the first generation after the Flood began; and the kingship [the capital] was in Kish."

5

Honors for the Lady Shub-ad

Out of her myths, her legends, her "king-lists," and her ruined cities has come Sumer's unexpected history. From them we learn what our grandparents never suspected: that early in the fourth millennium (4000-3000) B.C.E., a pastoral and agricultural people of great potential pushed its way into the southern end of the Tigris-Euphrates valley. Although the newcomers did not drive out the Semites who were there before them, these Sumerian immigrants soon became the dominant group. It was the Sumerians who covered the lower valley systematically with a network of canals and thus increased the acreage that could be cultivated. It was the Sumerians who built durable houses and temples out of baked clay bricks and raised the banks of the two rivers to protect their homes against flood damage. It was the Sumerian language that spread throughout the entire "land between the rivers" and was used in its written records. It was Sumerian literature that gave us some of our oldest Bible stories. And it was the Sumerians who brought the uses of copper and bronze and gold and tin and many kinds of stone and wood into the country, advanced the country's arts and crafts, and increased trading with foreign lands.

Sumer's cities were too self-governing, too independent, to submit without jealousies to an over-all pattern of government. They quarreled among themselves over water rights but joined forces to keep the flood walls and canals in repair lest the river overwhelm them or the canals dry up and the water fail to reach their irrigated fields. They fought over sources of raw materials and over markets for their goods but were quick to present a united front in the event of foreign invasion. To control the water, to regulate trade, and to defend the country, they banded their resources together under the leadership of the strongest city.

At first the Semites and the Sumerians had bartered for

31

their raw materials. Soon, at home and abroad, they were taking them by force. Now, in the storerooms of each city's temple, weapons for the populace were stored along with the sickles and the seed.

It was the cities' *gods* who fought each other, and not just the people alone, the Sumerians said. If the god won, his effigy was carried through the streets in triumph. If the city lost, the god's effigy was carried away among the spoils of victory. Success in war increased the god's prestige and the priests' popularity. The ambitions of the gods' administrators grew. Trade expanded. Wars continued. A thirst for empire developed. Now the priest who served as earthly counterpart for the city's god threw off the modest title of "tenant farmer of the god" and became "king" as well.

For twenty-three consecutive "kingships" "after the Flood" Kish was the greatest of Sumer's cities and each of her kings in turn regarded himself as king of all Sumer. Then, according to the "king-lists,"[19] the city of Erech gained supremacy and held the "kingship" during the reign of twelve more kings. Finally, the city of Ur seized the power, held it, lost it, and held it again in three distinct dynasties in the next six hundred years. (It was in the first of these three dynasties, some time before and after 2500 B.C.E., that Sumerian civilization reached its peak and in the third — about 1900 B.C.E. — that Abraham was probably born.)

Thus the fourth millenium, with all its primitive inventions and discoveries, gave way to the rivalries and expansions of the third.[20] And with the third (3000-2000 B.C.E.) was ushered into Sumer a taste for elegance and pomp, and even barbarity, in strange contrast to the simple contentment of what had once been only a pastoral and agricultural people. Yet this elegance and this barbarity, long unsuspected by historians and archaeologists, might not yet be known had it not been for the chance discovery, in 1927, of the so-called "royal tombs" of the First Dynasty of Ur (about 2500 B.C.E.).

Excavators came upon "the royal tombs of Ur" as a complete surprise in a cemetery that, itself, lay buried under layers of rubbish just outside the site which Sir Leonard Woolley had

Head of Shub-ad with jewels (restored).

already identified as the old city of Ur. It was the same cemetery and the same rubbish heap, in fact, below which the same
archaeologist discovered evidence of Ur's mighty flood. The
tombs were found and excavated, under the directorship of Sir
Leonard Woolley,[21] by joint expeditions of the British Museum
and the University of Pennsylvania Museum.

The elegance of the tombs lay in their luxurious furnishings, all showing, by their exotic materials, how far afield war
and trade had taken the Sumerians and, by their beauty, how
skilful Sumer's artisans had become. There were gold daggers
and helmets; a saw and a set of chisels also made of gold; and
there were exquisitely designed cups, bowls, jars, and little
boxes made of gold, silver, copper, and alabaster. There were
thousands of necklace beads made of carnelian, lapis lazuli,
agate, and equally precious stones, as well as gold and silver;
and jewelry and articles of personal use. There were two silver
tables among the furnishings; and there were musical instruments inlaid with mosaics and similarly decorated gaming
boards — for royal entertainment in another world.

More spectacular than the elegance of the furnishings,
however, was the evidence of barbarity that came to light in
the tomb of *the Lady Shub-ad*. Shub-ad had been an honored
woman — her name was found on a lapis lazuli cylinder seal;
but whether she was queen or priestess, one can not surely
say. Nor can it be known for certain whether hers was a natural
death or if she died a victim of religious sacrifice. In either
case, it would appear that members of her court or priesthood
had willingly followed her in death, expecting thereby to remain in her service and under her royal, or divine, protection.
For not only the Lady Shub-ad had died, but some twenty-five
attendants lay buried with her; and these, unquestionably, were
human sacrifices.

Five defenders, armed with copper daggers at their waists,
had guarded the entrance to an inner chamber of her tomb.
Within that chamber, the bejeweled body of the Lady Shub-ad
had lain on a wooden bier, with one attendant at her head and
another at her feet. The animals and grooms whose services
had drawn the bier into the tomb on a richly decorated sledge-
chariot had remained in the outer chamber to do their lady's

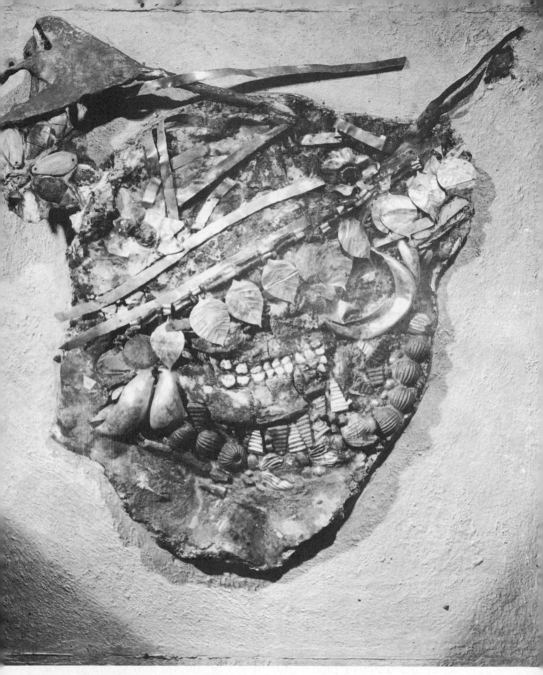

Skull of a lady-in-waiting, showing ornaments *in situ*, found in
Queen Shub-ad's burial chamber.

bidding in a world to come. Her ladies-in-waiting were also there, their jeweled headdresses and many necklaces reflecting the splendor and beauty of their mistress' adornments. Their ten bodies were arranged in two parallel rows, at the foot of which lay the remains of a beautiful harp; and across the harp, the body of Shub-ad's faithful harpist.

There was no sign of struggle among the tomb's arrangements: the Lady Shub-ad's headdress, as well as those of her ladies, was strictly in place. Though crushed by the weight of earth that had covered the tombs, its ornaments were intact, even to the flowered finials of her high, "Spanish type" comb. Nine yards of thin gold ribbon were entwined among the ornaments of what had been her massive, black wig. Beads of precious stones and metals had completely covered a short cloak that had reached to her waist and been held in place by three long, gold pins with heads of lapis lazuli. Wide, golden crescents had hung from her ears. They were so large that the crescents dipped almost to her shoulders, their gold so exquisitely ruddy that one is tempted to say he has never seen gold until he has seen these lunettes.

Close to the Lady's side (as was common practice in burials) lay her golden cup, the perfection of its line and color even now unbelievably superb. It would appear that from smaller, individual cups, and to music of their own making, her faithful followers may have drunk a fatal narcotic and, singing, composed themselves for death.

There were other "royal" tombs and "death pits" — one with a mass burial of as many as sixty-three persons — in that cemetery, as well as the simple graves of commoners without attendants or furnishings. And the royal tombs varied in size.

Every article in Lady Shub-ad's tomb, from the tiniest gold tweezers to the largest harp, was suitably ornamented. Gemstudded flower petals and inlays of animal and geometric designs were skilfully employed. Many of the pieces showed intricately fashioned details of ornamentation such as tiny ropes and spirals and rosettes and symbolically conceived embellishments, all of which enrich, but never detract from, the total effect of elegance and beauty.

Three gold vessels and harp (restored) from Shub-ad's tomb.

Gold was used in profusion, silver for emphasis. Copper was commonplace. Inlays of mother-of-pearl, carved limestone, and shell were common. With some articles, line was more important than decoration, but, again and again, unexpected little ornamental details were added. Never blatant, these details show imaginative freshness that suggests happy craftsmen. Even humor played its part in the artisans' designs.

It is difficult to picture a society which, on one hand, sanctioned human sacrifice apparently with joy and equanimity, while, on the other, its culture shows such artistic sensitivity that critics agree on this point: the beauty of its artisans' work has not been surpassed, *in any age of art,* in well over four thousand years!

And what shall be our interpretation of the so-called

"Standard of Ur," found in one of the other royal tombs in the same cemetery? In mosaics, on one side it depicts the harrowing scenes of War — soldiers equipped with axes, spears, and javelins; and naked prisoners, their arms bound, brought before the king or dragged to death beneath the feet of blood-excited animals — and on the other, scenes of Peace, with the king and his family sitting down to a banquet, attended by musicians and waited upon by servants, his people wearing the simple, sheepskin kilt of early Sumerians? Someone had to carve those figures from shell before they could be set in their lapis lazuli background on the "Standard." Someone had to feel the actions they portrayed. Someone had to contrast, in his own mind, the passions of War and the fruits of Peace. Or was it only Victory? Who made the "Standard of Ur," and for whom? We do not know.

The use, in the tombs' furnishings, of such precious stones as lapis lazuli, agate, carnelian, and alabaster, as well as gold and silver, bespeaks the distance from which raw materials were being brought for Sumer's royal artisans. Their use speaks, too, of the importance in which the Lady Shub-ad's life and death were held, and of the magnificence of her funeral rites. Yet by how little can we comprehend the thoughts of the Sumerians who witnessed such ceremonies.

If, in imagination, we could reconstruct Shub-ad's death and burial, what a story it would make! Ur would be a busy, growing city with a temple inside its walls and a cemetery just outside. Farms and orchards would stretch beyond the city between canals and the river, and the high towers of other cities' temples would be visible on the sky line. And here, by the muddy Euphrates, under a cloudless sky, we should watch an ancient Sumerian pageant come to life. Our eyes would feast on splendor. Our ears would ring with exotic chants. Our mouths would be dry with the taste of dust; our throats would be tight with emotion. There would be a fresh breeze from the river mingled with the odor of sweating bodies and excited animals; the stench, perhaps, of Ur's unsanitary streets if, on its way to the cemetery, the procession wound through the city proper. And with it all, there would be color and music and the fumes of incense.

The waiting crowds, the exotic music, the colorful cortege; priests in magnificent regalia, soldiers wearing bronze helmets and long capes, gayly clad guards; pompous, uniformed officials; and even commoners in sheepskin kilts bringing up the rear; the arrival of the Lady Shub-ad's bier drawn on a sledge by two sacrificial asses, the silver and electrum ornaments of their harnesses catching their last reflection of the sun; the self-importance of the royal grooms and guards, the mourning of the populace — all these, we would picture if we could.

Most spectacular of all would be Shub-ad's jewel-decked body drawn on the beautiful sledge and accompanied by her excited ladies-in-waiting. They would be wearing red woolen coats, embroidered with beads, and elaborate headdresses that were modified versions of their mistress' heavily ornamented wig.[22] But even more impressive than the procession would be the long drawn-out ceremonies at the grave itself.

The fervor of the day, the pathos, the exultation would be there, and even the treachery. For there was treachery — at least, that is how it would appear. Excavators found that the Lady Shub-ad's wardrobe box had been placed in such a way as to cover a gaping hole in the floor of her tomb's chamber, and the hole led to another, and larger, tomb — a king's tomb, the king's burial having been at some earlier date. Investigating, they discovered that the earlier tomb had been robbed of all but a few choice treasures which the robbers, in their haste, had overlooked. It had been plundered, perhaps, by the very persons who had been entrusted to "set the stage" in the inner chamber of Shub-ad's tomb for the Lady Shub-ad's burial. They had used the wardrobe box to cover the evidence of their depredations.

The ceremonies of burial would be long and in keeping with the elegance and barbarity of the times. But there was no sign of violence. We ask ourselves: what god inspired such ritual, what faith and loyalty excited such extremities of passion that men and women could willingly die in expectation of who-knows-what rewards?

The life that the furnishings of "the royal tombs of Ur" suggest was not common forty-five centuries ago. Indeed, we have to remember that, however barbaric its practices seem

Bull's head from a harp found in the King's tomb at Ur.

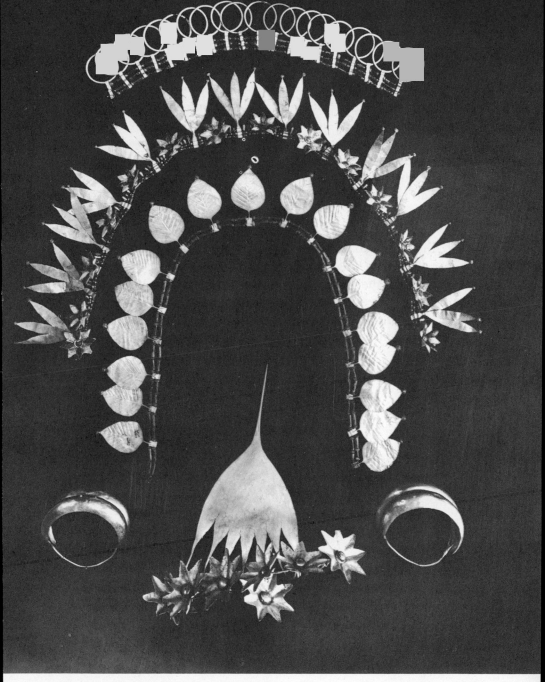

Jewelry and ornaments of Queen Shub-ad.

to us today, life in Sumer in Shub-ad's day was, in fact (like its Egyptian counterparts), a rare example of *advanced* civilization. It was a splash of luxury in a world much of which was still living under Stone Age conditions.

Until Shub-ad's tomb was discovered by Sir Leonard Woolley, no one had dreamed that Ur had passed through a period of such elegance. It had been at the height of Ur's prosperity and power as a capital city that she and her court had lavishly lived and sumptuously died. By the time of Abraham, Shub-ad and all her glory were long since gone. Gone, too, were the days when Sumer's empire had stretched from the Tigris to the Mediterranean Sea. Six hundred years had passed. Ur was no longer Sumer's foremost city. Her fortunes were on the wane. The royal tombs and the cemetery outside the city were already long forgotten. It was now the early nineteenth century B.C.E., and a group of shabby houses covered the forgotten site of the Lady Shub-ad's last honors!

6

Abraham and the Images

There was a boy, growing up in the city of Ur at about this time, whose father was said to have been a manufacturer of images. According to the same tradition, the boy peddled the images in the streets of Ur from a tray hung from his neck.

The little figures, about the size of your hand, were crudely made. They were shaped like men and women or like animals or birds. A few were fashioned from wood and stone, but most of them were molded out of soft clay and then baked in a pottery oven to make them hard. The people of Ur bought the images to set against a wall in the intimate, family chapels of their homes and to carry to new homes if they moved away. They wanted something that looked back at them and seemed to listen when they prayed that the gods would protect and guide them and "show the way."

The *moon* had "shown the way" when, long years before, Abraham's ancestors had lived on the open plains of northern Mesopotamia. There, the moon itself had assured primitive people that a great, unexplainable power constantly "watched over" them. But now, men said, the moon was *a god* seated in a high temple, watching over the city of Ur. That idea was not as comforting to the common people as the moon itself had been to the ancient shepherds and farmers in the days before men lived in cities.

This city god, with an imposing statue set in the high tower of the temple, often seemed too far away and too concerned with the problems of *the city* to recognize the needs of the bakers and brewers and brick-makers and all the rest of the "little" people. So the people set up smaller shrines with smaller statues for lesser gods whose chapels might be found in any street of Ur. But in spite of the lesser gods who, they believed, were concerned each with some special phase of their lives, misfortunes still fell upon them from time to time. Then they made still smaller images and set them in chapels within their homes. The image was not exactly a god, of course, but *it represented* the great, mysterious guiding power. And these were the images, the little household gods, the *teraphim* so called, that the boy was peddling in the streets of Ur in the early nineteenth century B.C.E. Thousands and thousands of them were sold all over Mesopotamia and Sumer; and today in Iraq, after more than four thousand years, you can find such images yourself, buried in the debris that now covers most of her ancient cities.

The boy peddling images in the streets of Ur was not necessarily Abraham, but he could have been. Nor was the father necessarily named Terah, but we shall call him so and show, from recent excavations, a little of what any boy *such as Abraham* might have seen and experienced in Ur *in the time of Abraham.*[23]

Ur's days of unbelievable splendor had passed. Her suburbs were shabby and old, and her irrigation canals were not as well tended as formerly. Her merchants complained that trade was not what it once had been. Loyalties were at such a low ebb that mercenaries were being hired to augment Ur's dwindling army. A growing Semitic influence from the north was undermining both government and trade. But, in spite of all this, Ur was still a busy city.

Outside the city wall lived Sumerian peasants, farmers, cattle-raisers, and slaves. Inside the city, men were more often traders, artisans, mechanics, factory workers, and merchants. Ur still sent caravans to far places. Her ships went in and out of the canals and up and down the Tigris and Euphrates rivers, unless blocked by Semitic competitors, and coastwise to ports of the wider seas.

There were two-story houses and factories, schools and shops in Ur at this time, and one great temple with a tower which dominated the city. This towered temple, this *ziggurat* (meaning "mountain top"), the Sumerians called *the House of the Great Light*. It was old in Abraham's day, having been built by the great King Ur-nammu[24] in honor of Nannar, moon-god of Ur.

Abraham's family was not Sumerian. His forebears were

presumably Semitic *Aramaeans* from the Balikh valley in north-western Mesopotamia. At some time they had migrated south-ward, attracted, no doubt, by the pasturelands and farms and orchards of Sumer, and by its busy markets. Ur was full of Semites as well as Sumerians. To Terah, Abraham's father, living in the Sumerian city of Ur, there was nothing incongruous in his loyalty to the city's god or to his use of the local shrines. Terah was a moon-worshiper — as his ancestors long before him had been. The difference was only in the Sumerian name, *Nannar,* given to the moon-god in the south.

City gods were common in Sumer. There was *Ishtar,* star-goddess of Erech, and *Shamash,* sun-god of Larsa, for example; and over all, so people believed, the early deities of "the river country," An and Enlil and Inanna. There were also many lesser deities. But, in Abraham's time, Nannar, the moon-god, "eldest son of Enlil," was supreme in Ur. The people believed that upon Nannar depended the peace, protection, and pros-perity of their city.

Since the god could not be expected to attend to the details and management of the large properties he controlled, the priests took it upon themselves to do it for him. They set aside the whole northwest corner of the city as a Sacred Area and fortress and made of it a high platform of earth and brick to keep out floods and invaders.

The Temenos, as they called this sacred area, was the moon-god's domain. It provided living and working quarters for his priests and servitors. It was a fortress to which, if Ur were attacked, the people might come as a last resort to fight for themselves and the priests under the protection of the god.

The temple was by no means the only building that stood on the huge, artificial platform that was the Temenos. There were smaller temples also, some of them elaborately decorated. There were storerooms and workshops and offices, all used in the service of the divine Nannar and his wife, *Nin-gal.* And since Nannar was "king" as well as god of Ur, there was a palace for his earthly representative, the high priest. Here, the earthly "king" sat for audiences on a throne with his back to a high wall, just as the image of the god sat high against a wall of the sanctuary at the very top of the *ziggurat.*[25]

Worshipper with offering of a kid.

In proportion to his means, everyone in Ur contributed to the moon-god's support. Farmers brought flax to the temple workrooms and shepherds, wool, to be woven into hangings by temple weavers who had already made Ur famous for its textiles. Merchants brought expensive importations of calcite or diorite, or even ivory, to be carved by the god's master craftsmen. Some worshipers brought herbs for the god's kitchen. Others brought the first fruits of their orchards or grain to be stored in the enormous bins provided for that purpose in the Temenos.

Sacrifice, of course, had long played a major part in the religious devotion of Ur's people. The animals they brought to the shrines were usually taken from their own herds and flocks, but, like the little clay *teraphim,* they could also be bought at Ur's noisy market place. Birds, too, were acceptable for sacrifice, and in demand. Sheep and goats were frequent contributions. Occasionally a wealthy man would bring an ox.

In the temple's kitchens, slaves, under the supervision of priests, killed the sacrificial animals and prepared and cooked the meat in huge, copper cauldrons. Part of the meat from these donations the priests dedicated to the god, some they shared with the donor, and the rest they themselves ate or used up in their households. They told the people that the gods "loved the sweet savor" of the cooking. So, in spite of the moon-god's remoteness and in addition to the more personal comfort they derived from their little household images and from simple services in their family chapels, the people of Ur continued to bring generous offerings to the Sacred Area which, every day, was crowded with men and beasts and merchandise.

When, on festival days, Terah stood with his sons on the edge of a crowd, in all the excitement of watching a procession pass by, he probably had few doubts as to Nannar's protecting powers. He could almost believe it was the god himself, and not the statue, that the gayly clad priests were taking from the lofty sanctuary in the temple and carrying down the long stairway in a procession on their way to the god's summer temple outside the heat-wracked city.

But if Abraham had daringly asked, as tradition suggests,

"How do we know the moon-god can take care of us?" Terah could not have answered. Not so many generations ago — but this was almost too painful to remember — Nannar had been unable to save even himself when his image had been seized from its holy place in the *ziggurat* and carried off to *Susa* by Elamite invaders. In time, the Elamites had returned the statue and helped to repair the temple (for they feared all gods), but the moon-god's prestige had suffered immeasurably among his own people.

If Abraham had persisted, "Will Nannar take care of you and me? Will he take care of my sick geese?", Terah would have advised, "Go to *Bau's* little sanctuary, my son, and take her a pot of clarified butter, and your geese will get well." At such a time, Abraham would hasten to the tiny wayside shrine of this patroness of the poultry farm. There, he would lay his problem and his offering before the small, squat, domestic figure of the goddess *Bau*, with her golden crown and with flounced skirts that reached to her ankles, as she sat heavily on a throne supported on the backs of her famous geese.[26]

The moon-god in the temple was great, the lesser gods at the wayside shrines were numerous and important, but more and more the people of Ur clung to their faith in the little family gods that they could turn to, face to face. They made chapels within their homes and set the little images in these sanctuaries. We call such images *teraphim,* although *teraphim* is a word not yet fully understood in translation. Scholars even suggest that the *teraphim* may have symbolized deceased ancestors to the family-conscious Sumerians. Such minor gods they represented, with powers so limited, people did not even name them. But to the family, *teraphim* became indispensable.

For were they not *gods,* the people would have said, and, being gods, were they not able to "divine" the future and in a position to appeal to even the most powerful deities in the family's behalf? With this line of reasoning, on to the shoulders of the little, unnamed, personal god, the family loaded the burden of its safety and success.

Men carved representations of the family god on cylinder seals on which a man's name or symbol was also engraved.

There he stood, drawn in angular lines, the little unnamed, unfamed, family god, dragging by the hand some member of the family; and in front of them sat the pompous, greater god — often the city god — clearly named or symbolized, to whom the little god had come to intercede. Literally, the *teraphim*, symbolizing the family god or a dead ancestor, "stood between" man and the all-powerful deity.

Now, because they wished to keep the family unit forever together under the protection of its own special god, the people of Ur gave up their use of cemeteries and grave furnishings and buried their dead under the floors of their homes and family chapels. In this way, they believed, living and dead, the long line of their family remained unbroken in that house. When they offered sacrifices in the family chapel, they believed that the offering they shared with the god also provided food for the dead. Everything in the house belonged as much to the dead members as to the living. With primitive naivete, they set a cup of water on the chapel's low, brick altar to keep the dead man's spirit safe and satisfied and happy to remain at home, lest, dangerously, it wander abroad and the retribution for the dead man's misdeeds fall upon living members of the family.

Large or small, dwelling houses in Ur in the nineteenth century B.C.E. were mostly of similar design. They were of much the same pattern, too, as many of the houses still built in Middle Eastern countries after four thousand years. Each house was built around an inner courtyard which provided a peaceful oasis from the confusions, clutter, heat and squalor of the city's narrow streets.[27]

But sometimes, in the least prosperous days, some of these two-story city houses, with their tall, narrow doorways and no windows opening on the street, were made over to include a shop and a salesroom. Such renovations, archaeologists have found, were not uncommon during the years of Ur's declining prosperity. A cook-shop in the bazaar was one example. There was a schoolhouse too that was a made-over house, one half being used by the master for a house and library, and the other

Archaic images from Mesopotamia.

— the reception room, lavatory, and courtyard — devoted to the school.

It is in the late, Jewish traditions of the *Book of Jubilees* (third century B.C.E. [28]) that Terah, the father of Abraham, has been called a merchant and a manufacturer of images. In that case, his house, too, might have been a dwelling made over to include a shop. And Abraham, his son, like many another boy, could indeed have sold images in the streets of Ur. Certainly we know that such trade could have been brisk in this city where the names of several *thousand* lesser gods have come to light and where *teraphim* were in general use. But to say that Abraham questioned the power of the *teraphim*, as stories in the *Book of Jubilees* suggest, is to put third-century B.C.E. ideas into an early nineteenth-century B.C.E. setting. Terah and Abraham had probably never known a family without its *teraphim*.

Some picturesque stories concerning Abraham were current when the *Book of Jubilees* was written. They were told by men who wanted to believe, and who wanted others to believe, that Abraham had had no other gods than One God Most High. In the light of the somewhat more advanced morality of their day, they wanted their hero to have been a man who stood out against the use of what they called *idols*. For the author of *Jubilees* to picture Abraham selling images under protest and for him to record that Abraham's zeal brought tragedy to Terah's family may have been no more than a dramatic expression of this same idea.

"Why do you worship these figures that have no heart and spirit in them?" they pictured Abraham as saying to his father. "They are the work of hands. Upon your shoulders do you carry them. You have no help from them. Do not kneel to them; worship the god in heaven who sends down the dew and rain upon the earth and has created every living thing."

But his father could only say, "Keep silent, my son, lest the people slay you for your words."

Finally, Abraham spoke to his two brothers in the same way he had pleaded with his father, and they, too, became angry at him; and he kept silent. Then (so the ancient *Jubilees* story continues) "Abraham arose in the night, and burned down the house of his idols, and burned all that was in the house, and there was no man that knew it. And they [his family] arose in the night and desired to save their idols from the midst of the flame. And [one of his brothers] ran in order to save them, and the fire burned over him and he burned in the midst of the fire, and he died in Ur of the Chaldees . . . and they buried him in Ur."[29]

Scholars remind us that such stories "represent no continuous tradition" and are probably more picturesque than true. However, for a boy to have sometimes questioned his father's beliefs was not sacrilege. It was natural. It was intelligent. How else has religion evolved and how else have saner concepts outdistanced primitive thinking except by each son's ideas standing on the shoulders of his father's convictions?

Even if the stories of what Abraham did to the images are truer to youth and to a third-century sense of morality than to fact, nonetheless they suggest something original and courageous in the character of Abraham. The world would give a good deal to know truly Abraham's own religious experience.

Excavating the *ziggurat* of Ur.

7

The Ziggurat of Ur

Seeing the ruins of the temple and the layout of the city and its environs, and considering the archaeological deductions, it is not difficult to imagine Abraham as a young boy living in Ur. On any afternoon he might have been found threading his way along a dusty path that ran between the shabby houses that, archaeologists say, covered the forgotten site of the Lady Shub-ad's grave in Abraham's time. Little he, or anyone else in Ur, suspected what history and what golden treasure even then lay under his feet in the "royal tombs" of a still earlier day! Let us say he was going from his father's farm, where the family grew vegetables and raised livestock outside the city proper, to the family home inside the wall. Perhaps, as he passed through the city, he would be leaving a gift offering of a dove at the temple of Nannar, moon-god of Ur.

Each pair of fledgling doves that hatched at the farm provided one bird for the moon-god and one for Terah's dovecote. The finest pigeon — or goose, or calf, or kid — was always "marked" for the god's share of the family good fortune. So the way from his father's farm to the Temenos was a familiar path to Abraham and his brothers.

Others might approach the Sacred Area from its formal, northeast entrance but, boy-like, Abraham had short cuts of his own. Through the muddy roads that crossed the fields he went; over the dump that covered the forgotten cemetery; through a gap in the city wall that had never been adequately repaired since Ur's last invasion; and into Ur's narrow streets. And ahead of him, all the way, loomed the high platform of the Temenos, crowned by the bulky *ziggurat*, the tower of Nannar's temple.

Visible from every corner of the city and for many miles out on the surrounding countryside, the outline of the *ziggurat* was as familiar to Abraham as the path that led to it. It stood high above the squalor and heat of the crowded city. It overlooked the Euphrates River and the sprawling canals that led to other Sumerian settlements — they, too, with temples and *ziggurats* that honored each its own god.

What a massive structure the *ziggurat* was, Abraham thought, as he walked along, facing it in the distance. Surely, only with the gods' help could it ever have been conceived! It rose like a stepped pyramid in four blocks, each block smaller than the one on which it stood. This allowed for terraces at every level — terraces planted with trees and shrubs, until the whole structure suggested a mountain on whose summit (the topmost block) was the shrine of the god. The first three blocks were built solid of earth and brick, but the summit was a room.

This summit room, people said, was the earthly home of the moon-god. It was the holiest of all sanctuaries of Ur. And this sanctuary, this shrine, this room at the top of the *ziggurat*, the Sumerians named *Heaven*.

Once, a great king rebuilt the summit room, facing its outer walls with blue-glazed bricks and crowning it with a small, golden dome. At the same time, the brick sides of the block just below the summit were glazed red and the sides of the two lowest blocks were painted black. Men liked to say that these colors, rising black, black, red, blue, and gold, symbolized the divisions of the universe: they were the underworld, the earth, and heaven; and to reach the house of God one must pass through all of them.[30]

Everything about the *ziggurat*, architecturally, led the eye upward. The building itself was rectangular, the shrine room square and flat-topped. The corners of the building pointed exactly north, east, south, and west, with the main approach on the northeast side.

Here, on the *ziggurat's* northeastern face, three impressive stairways of one hundred steps each — designed to heighten the spectacular effect of the priests' colorful processions — met in a great vestibule on the level of the second terrace; and from this, two smaller stairways led back to the first. Numerous other brick staircases and ramps, irregularly placed, connected the several levels of the "holy mountain." But the main stairway

Ziggurat of Ur, northeast façade, showing stairways.

went straight on, through the vestibule, up and up, until, like a ladder linking earth and heaven, it reached the shrine.

Yes, the house of the god they called Heaven. And the *ziggurat*, with its long staircase, was to the Sumerians a ladder linking Heaven and Earth. It was easy for them to believe all this, especially when they viewed the *ziggurat* from a distance.[31]

As he made his way into the city, Abraham looked down at the lively bird that lay in his arms, gently pecking the back of his hand. Such a tiny gift to be bringing to such an important god! He remembered the hungry little skin-and-bones the dove had been only a few weeks before. Not even down had covered its nakedness when it was hatched. Now it was sleek and soft and more politely ravenous — the finest bird he had ever raised, he boasted to himself. Today he was bringing it, a proper gift, however small, to the moon-god. From the pocket of his tunic Abraham drew half a handful of hemp seeds. A pigeon can get so excited over hemp seeds!

As usual, Ur's streets were crowded and hot. Porters, their backs bent double under the weight of heavily laden sacks,

Stela of Ur-Nammu, who built the *ziggurat* at the God's "command."

staggered past him carrying merchandise from the docks into the city for storage in the owner's warehouse. Donkeys plodded along, balancing twin burdens; occasionally they blocked Abraham's passage in the narrow streets. Which of the importations the porters and the donkeys carried would become gift offerings for the god who had brought them safely to port? Abraham wondered. And what did the bundles and bales contain?

Soon he had crossed the city and was within the Sacred Area. He hurried along the "Sacred Way," past the palace designed by Ur-nammu, the king, whom "the gods had instructed" to build the *ziggurat;* past the limestone stela five feet wide and perhaps fifteen high, that recorded the story of the building; past smaller temples built for Nannar and his wife, Nin-gal, till he stood at last within the first courtyard of the great Temple of Nannar.

One was never prepared for the extent of this courtyard or for the confusions it contained. Here, men brought their animals or their cheeses, their butter or their grain to pay rent for the land or the sickles or the seed; or to offer them as gifts to the god. Altogether it was as noisy and as busy as a market place and there was little about its activities to suggest the sacred nature of the place. Perhaps it was on the courtyard just above that sanctity prevailed.

On the stairs that led to the second courtyard, Abraham paused. To the south, orchards and farms and pasture lands sprawled between man-made waterways. To the north, a line of waving palm trees outlined the course of the great river that fed all Ur's canals.

Looking north, Abraham asked himself, *where does the great river come from?* and south, *Once it reaches the sea, what then?* The birds knew. How widespread was the world and how exciting to think about, once a boy climbed above the confusions of the crowded city! Almost, he was tempted to let his dove fly free.

His mother considered it a privilege to offer one of each pair of pigeons to the moon-god. "You cannot forever keep for yourself one little, well-marked bird," she would say, "but

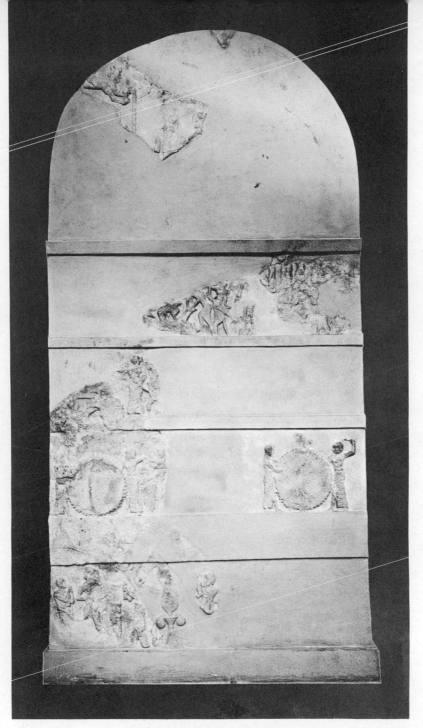

Stela of Ur-Nammu, reverse.

Ruins of the *ziggurat* of Ur.

the tablet which the god's clerk will give you as proof of payment, *that* you can keep and treasure as long as you live." And
his father would add that in giving anything to the moon-god
one was but giving back to Nannar what the god had already
given him.

Remembering all this, up the stairs Abraham went with
the other worshipers, his loudly throbbing heart beating a swift
accompaniment to the pigeon's gentler pulse.

The entry at the top of the stairs was the threshold to the
forecourt of the *ziggurat*, and here Abraham took his place in
a line of gift-laden men and women. No one with a gift or a
payment was allowed to pass into the courtyard until a clerk
had recorded the transaction and given him a receipt for his
contribution. Waiting his turn, Abraham had a chance to look
around.

The *ziggurat*, when viewed at close range, was a surprise.
Now the great height gave way to breadth — a massive, brick
building whose bulk one had hardly expected to be so great.
The levels of its terraces were so lofty (the first was thirty-five
feet from the courtyard's pavement) and the main stairway so
unbelievably impressive, that the priests whom Abraham could

see moving about on the high terraces seemed to him to be men of a mysterious world and infinitely close to the moon-god.

On the sunny side of this court, some women were bleaching linen that had been woven on royal looms; others were carding wool; and on the shady side, two other women sat in front of a doorway, grinding corn between two stones, quite oblivious of what went on around them. Men with animals and goods crossed the court in the direction of the storerooms and kitchens. In the foreground, a balky goat that was to have been a sacrifice to Nannar kept straining on the rope that led him, as if he knew his fate and sought to avoid the honor. In the distance a procession was just passing out of sight, the sound of its music rising, now loud, now soft, until it died away.

The line of gift-bearers shortened and moved nearer to the recording clerks' desk. Abraham too advanced, holding the lively pigeon close to his body. He smoothed its neck gently with his fingers, his hand dodging its beak's short, sharp pecks. Perhaps the bird was still hungry, he thought, fishing in his pocket for one last tidbit. By this time the dove was already so full of hemp seed it was intoxicated, but its antics only endeared it the more to its young owner.

Somewhere across the court, a bull roared. So small, so very small, his little squab, no more than a taste-tempter at the god's feast, Abraham thought. Did the moon-god really need his dove? "It is for Nannar," he kept repeating to himself.

The line continued to shorten until only one man stood between Abraham and the clerk. It was exciting to be next in line, and impressive to be bringing his payment to the moon-god of Ur. One by one in line ahead of him, Nannar's proud supporters had departed with their receipts, while couriers carried off to its proper storage space the gift or payment each had made. A bowl of barley, a basket of onions, a bundle of wool, a lively goat, a pot of clarified butter, a mina of silver or even a shekel of gold — these were the visible evidence of the reverence and support the god's subjects gladly gave to Nannar. There was another evidence, however, invisible and quite as impressive. That was the imagination and creative skill which went into fashioning another type of gift offering for Nannar — the handicrafts of his people.

In front of Abraham stood an old man holding a bulky, sizeable package wrapped in a worn, woven cloth. It was round as a ball, and light in spite of its size. Abraham was curious to see the package unwrapped.

With hands that trembled, the old man drew back the cloth. Even then Abraham could not name the gift. It was a good deal like a ball, he thought, a hollow ball, made of hundreds of little spindles, with a braided grass ring at the top; but too large and somewhat frail to be tossed about. He tried to listen while the man explained how long he had worked on his offering and how happy he was to present it to Nannar for use in one of the temples of the god or the god's wife.

"One by one I collected twigs from the marshes each spring when the wood was pliant and green," he explained, quaintly, "always just so big they must be, so big and no more. Then I peeled and bleached the wood and gathered a supply of soft reeds for tying. On the days when first the new moon hung like a sickle in the afternoon sky, I wove the wet twigs together and tied them into shape with the soft reeds. It has taken me a long time — many years I have labored on it. Now I am old and I bring the work of my hands to the moon-god, praying that I, too, like the moon, may be born again after death."

"Your gift is beautiful," said the clerk kindly. "The workmanship is exquisite. You have brought a fine offering." Still Abraham did not know what the gift was. He stood staring at it, scarcely aware that the hopeful old man had pocketed his receipt and was departing.

It was Abraham's turn — so sudden, he had not time to be either joyous or sad at parting with his bird. Automatically the clerk reached into a basket by his side and drew out a fresh tablet of soft clay — an inch or two wide it was and twice as long, and shaped like a miniature pillow. Using a stiff reed stylus about the size of a pencil, with rapid strokes he forced little, wedge-shaped impressions into the moist clay. The clerk asked Abraham his name and his father's name, dug more impressions into the tablet, and then looked up to see what kind of an offering he must record below the names.

Meanwhile, the courier who was supposed to be taking the

old man's gift away had lingered to admire Abraham's dove
and to laugh at the antics of a pigeon delirious from too much
hemp seed.

"She is a smart one, she is; and round as a little fat cheese,"
the courier said.

"The best marked pigeon in the flock," Abraham explained,
proudly.

"How old?"

"Four weeks tomorrow."

The courier seemed to know something about pigeon-
raising. "She's scarcely more than off the nest," he said.

"That's when they eat best," the clerk put in. "When their
wings have never known flight, that's when they eat best. Only
a mouthful, but juicy and tender, and pink as a shrimp." Abraham agreed, stroking the dove with a finger that followed the
pattern of its markings.

He knew it had to happen. Was he not glad to be able to
bring this tiny contribution to the god who dwelt in the House
of the Great Light? What a silly he was, just because there was
a cold spot in his tunic where the dove no longer lay! Suddenly
he was aware of words the courier was saying to the clerk, as
together they appraised the bird with critical attention.

"Much *too* good; and, as you say, only a mouthful at best.
But alive — just what the priest wants: he needs all the beautiful ones he can get for breeding stock."

The clerk drew back the tablet he was on the point of
giving Abraham. With a wide sweep of a well-practiced
thumb, he erased the last words of the inscription by smoothing
his thumb over the still moist clay. Then, on the smoothed surface he reworded the record he wished to make. When the
clay had had time to harden, the record would be clear and
indelible. "Abraham, son of Terah," had presented to the god
Nannar on such and such a day, "one silver-colored, blue-striped
dove for breeding stock at the royal poultry farm."

Abraham could not believe it. No one was going to eat
his little squab after all! The dove was so perfect the god
wanted it to produce more and more birds as beautiful as itself.
The boy was delighted.

"And while we are about it, why not put the dove in the

old man's bird cage until we have a singing bird to hang in the queen's hall?" he heard the clerk continue.

And the last Abraham saw of his groggy little hemp-filled pigeon that was to have given its life as his payment to Nannar was the courier disappearing through the crowd, swinging the beautiful willow bird cage by its braided grass handle, with Abraham's tiny dove crouched safely at the bottom of the cage.

8

Twilight and Dawn

Quite out of breath, Abraham reached his city home. In haste he splashed water over his feet and legs, as he passed through the vestibule of the house, and dried his feet by scuffing across the open courtyard. He had noticed that his father was not in the shop, so he headed across the court toward the kitchen, drawn by the spicy aromas which rose from pots steaming on the cookstove.

To his right were quarters for the servants, their brick bedsteads visible through an open door. Beyond these, outside, were the customary sheds for animals and storage space.

To Abraham's left, stairs led to a balcony which overhung all four sides of the courtyard. Here were family rooms and here was access to further living space on the flat housetop, awning-sheltered by day from the heat of the sun.

On the ground floor level, one side of the house was occupied by a reception room which also fronted on the courtyard — a long, narrow room where friends could range themselves along a wall for an informal chat or where beds could be improvised for those who might stay overnight.

Abraham soon became aware that his father was entertaining guests in this reception room. A lively discussion was in progress. Men's voices rose and fell, not with the gentle cadence of traditional hospitality, but with sharp, staccato barks of annoyance, accompanied by a rumble of gloomy bass notes.

A servant came out of the kitchen, his short tunic gleaming white in the sunshine. He had a tray of sweetmeats in his hands and was about to cross the courtyard when Abraham interrupted his passage.

"What's going on?" Abraham asked, indicating the direction of the voices by a twist of his head. The servant shrugged his shoulders and attempted to avoid the boy, but not before Abraham had helped himself to a handful of dates. "I don't know," he said. "It's the same as goes on all the time these days."

Abraham followed him across the court and stood outside the door of the reception room, listening, his back flat against the house wall. The bricks were cool to his back, but his breath was hot with excitement.

"We are getting nowhere by delaying," one man was saying dully.

A lively argument followed.

"Would you leave your own father beneath the threshold, and he not dead the space of a moon's cycle?"

"Aye, and my father would be the first to say, 'Go!' My father was a trader; no man ever robbed his caravans."

"Where there are no markets, I say, who can trade?"

"Where there are no materials, who can manufacture?"

". . . No wealth, who can buy?"

"No northerner is going to block my routes; I say we fight!"[32]

"We have fought; has that brought back the cargoes?"

"These northerners want to get rid of our businesses, lest we compete in their markets."

"It is not only the northerners. I have my trouble right here in Ur."

"It is the same with me. My best workman! He begs to accompany a caravan north just once, to see for himself the silver markets and the forests he has heard about. And does he return? No. To the cities he goes and hires himself out at fancy wages to men who admire the beauty of his jewelry work and the profits they can make out of him."

"Markets in the north are brisk."

"The stars draw the workmen north."

So the conversation went until the same dull voice repeated, "We are gaining nothing by delaying."

Then a sharp, excited voice that Abraham wished he could identify spoke on a high pitch. "Dead or no dead, I'm taking my family north!"

Abraham tiptoed a few feet away from the door, then flew to the stairway. He found his mother gathering up seeds she had been drying on a straw tray on the housetop.

"Mother, Mother," he demanded, "what is happening? What is Father saying to those men downstairs?"

His mother laughed. "What *is* he saying? Do I have the ears of a donkey that I may hear the brayings of the herd? You came that way: what *was* he saying?" she finished with curiosity.

"Northern markets, that's what he is saying!"

"He is worried, and more so every day." There was no longer laughter in her voice.

Abraham continued. "Someone is heading north with his family. I think it is the harness-maker. And somebody's goldsmith has run away. And someone is going to leave the bodies of his dead forefathers behind him in Ur! Are we?"

"Hush, son, none of us are going north," she faltered, scooping her seeds into a pottery jar with a motion that hid her trembling face behind her arm, "at least, not unless your father . . . says . . . we are. . . ."

"Why, Mother, you are crying. We *are* going north. And I shall be a trader and go to Mari and Harran and Kanish, and — who can say — even to the Great Sea where the Egyptian rafts load cedar logs."

"Not so fast, my son. Would you leave all we have here and become *'Apiru* — footloose and without a settled home — for the sake of the palace trade at Mari or the silver markets of Kanish?"

"But, Mother, would you not like to go north?"

His mother brushed the tears from her eyes, struggling to be fair.

"You go in the dawn, young Abraham," she said, "and you carry your treasure, which is your youth, in a light knapsack on your back; but we who go in the twilight of our years, our hearts are heavy laden. Our saddle bags are weighted with regrets: yet it is only a caravan of memories we take with us. We go north leaving our real treasure behind, too hidden to assemble, too rooted to transplant, and soon the darkness claims it. You are young, my son. Look up. Trust in the gods, and if your father says we go, we shall go with the gods' blessings."[33]

9

Farewell to Ur, Farewell to Sumer

How long it took, in months and years, for Terah to make up his mind to leave Ur, we cannot say. Long enough, the Book of Genesis tells us, for his sons to have grown to manhood and married. Long enough — the traditions of the *Book of Jubilees* would have us believe — for one of his sons to have died defending the images and leaving a son named Lot.[34] Long enough, in short, for Terah's family to have tasted the sweet wines of three marriage feasts and to have drunk the bitter dregs of tragedy. Yet, whether it was some such family tragedy as the death of Abraham's brother or whether it was the dwindling markets of Ur that sent Terah northward, we cannot now be certain.

It is scarcely possible that his migration was an isolated trek to Harran, made by his family alone. Other families, too, were on the move. They were caught in a wave of economic pressures that, sooner or later, sent many adventurous families northward and to the west. They were caught in a mesh of political uncertainties in Sumer.

Whatever the reasons that influenced Terah's decision, we may be sure that, in leaving Ur, it was with his religious connections he found it most difficult to part. Beneath the floor of his home chapel lay at least some of his family dead. In the cupboard beside the altar were stacked important family records. As senior member of the family, Terah would continue to be its priest and law-maker, but Nannar and Ur's lesser gods and his own family chapel would be left behind. Only the little images of the household god, the *teraphim*, could he take with him to guide and protect his family.

Such a move required considerable preparation. Tents, blankets, clothing; tools and weapons; food and utensils and skins for water; all must be made ready for the journey. Mounts and pack animals must be provided. Terah's local wealth must

School tablet, with problems in square root.

be turned into portable possessions. When all this was done, there were still debts to be paid and *Good-byes* to be said — to neighbors and friends, to members of the family remaining in the city, to the deities of Ur. We can only imagine the scene.

Finally, the day of departure came.

Terah and his family knelt for the last time in the family chapel. Already, together, the family had sacrificed two of its finest animals before the altars of Nannar and Nin-gal and offered simpler sacrifices at the shrines of several of Ur's minor gods. But for the goddess of travelers, *Pa-sag*, and for the great god in the *ziggurat*, there must be final gifts as well. It was not enough that a man leaving Ur should take with him his cylinder seal engraved with the symbol of his family god. That was his passport, his calling card. But if he wished to ensure a safe journey, he would also bring gifts to this goddess of travelers.

For the last time, Terah made his way through the streets of Ur, with all their familiar sights[35] and sounds, on his way to Pa-sag's shrine. Smoke was coming from the stoke-room as he passed the coppersmith's house; the smell of fresh bread baking came from the cook-shop. In the courtyard of the inn, several tethered asses stood patiently waiting for their masters and, as usual, the watchdog of the inn sat chained to his kennel at the little entrance court. There were students droning their lessons in the elementary school[36] as he passed it and a pile of their discarded clay exercise tablets had been swept, untidily, into the street almost in front of Pa-sag's door. Their reading and music lessons were mostly parts of the temple rituals, chants, and hymns. For mathematics, they had problems in multiplication and division. (In a more advanced school there would be exercises in practical geometry and problems in square and cube root.) There were also literary texts to be copied and memorized. Now it was a lesson in grammar that was going on: the children were fairly shouting the conjugation of Sumerian verbs.

Pa-sag's was a modest chapel, containing two statues of the goddess and an assortment of gifts. Its door was flanked by two grotesque terra-cotta figures, half man, half beast, each holding a spear. People said these gods would turn away disaster from all who passed between them.

School tablet, reverse.

For the last time, Terah entered and looked around Pa-sag's simple chapel.[37] How gaudily painted was the limestone statue of the goddess, how shiny her gilt crown! How stark the skull of the long-horned buffalo that hung on a peg on the wall above the goddess' head! Long had it hung there, proud evidence of at least one costly sacrifice at a humble, shabby shrine.

Terah passed the large statue and the whitened skull and proceeded to the sanctuary at the far end of the tiny court, where a brick table or altar awaited his offering. Here, another statue of Pa-sag, little more than a foot high, graced the holy spot. It was battered and blackened from the buffeting it had received — when the Elamites had burned the city, perhaps — but doubly precious for its scars.

Terah's gift was a clay model of one of his own carts. Prayerfully, he laid it on the offerings' table. And so he left Pa-sag, Ur's goddess of travelers, and passed between the statues, half man, half beast, and through the chapel door.

There could be no turning back now. Terah was leaving Ur. Already assembled, his caravan waited outside the city wall. More than that: he was leaving *Sumer* and all the familiar highways and waterways and markets and temples of the neighboring cities where he had traded for many years.

In thoughtful mood, Terah reached the Temenos and the moon-god's temple. "Here is a man come to say *Good-bye* to you, great Nannar!" his heart cried out, but the jostling crowds in the Temenos failed to notice his emotion; "here is a man come to say *Good-bye* to Ur, *Good-bye* to Sumer!" but the noisy taxpayers brushed him by as just another rich worshiper with a gift for the offerings' table.

Of what was Terah thinking when, for the last time, he scanned the flat Sumerian horizon from the staircase of Ur's "holy mountain?" Not of the markets of Larsa, Ur's turbulent rival to the northeast. Not of the decaying temple of el Obeid, whose glittering decorations still shone in the sunshine four miles to the west of him. Not of the gods of Eridu, the oldest of all Sumer's settlements, the peak of whose ancient *ziggurat* just broke the southern coastline.

Let Larsa prevail; let el Obeid's neglected temple still glitter and glow or let it fade under a mound of accumulating

Two friezes from the Temple of El Obeid, showing bulls and milking scene.

debris for all Terah cared now. Beyond him ran the Euphrates River, stretching its high-piled banks, fringed with vegetation, into that same northern land from which his forefathers were said to have come. Terah's memories were of Sumer, perhaps, but his eyes turned ever northward, like the needle to the star.

And what of Abraham, waiting with the caravan outside the city wall? He, too, was leaving Ur, the home of his childhood. No more would he visit his father's farm and carry offerings to Nannar or elbow his way through Ur's market place, amused by the jargon and jabberings of foreign traders. The path of the caravan would lead Terah's family through broad plains, only occasionally dotted with cities. Living in tents, traveling often by moonlight, Abraham would taste the solitude that had inspired his ancestors. Of that he knew nothing. It was enough for him that the caravan would be heading up the valley of the mighty Euphrates. It was the river and the mystery of the mountains he had never seen that, like a magnet, were drawing a willing Abraham north.

From the red walls of the *ziggurat,* Terah looked up to the sacred summit of the moon-god's shrine. Perhaps he knelt as he laid his last gifts on the offerings' table — for Nannar, a copper basin ringed with a circle of silver crescents; and, for Nin-gal, a rare vase that had come from Susa — alabaster, it was, its sides as thin as a shell and as translucent as moonlight through a fog. Terah was saying *Good-bye forever* to the city of Ur at the shrine of the city's protector.

At last he turned away from the shrine and down the great stairway that reached from "Heaven" to Earth, down, down, he went, across the courtyard, through the gates — into a new world.

The dust rose like a gigantic tent where Terah's animals stamped their restless feet. Here the family also waited; its members impatient for Terah's arrival. At his approach, the party roused itself, the herdsmen made ready. Terah signaled for his mount and drew his head coverings more closely to shade his eyes from the swirling dust.

The occasion was much too solemn for random conversation. Among the older members of the party scarcely a word was exchanged, but out in front, the enthusiasms of youth burst

Ziggurat of Ur, showing recessed panels of its massive foundation.

into lively shouts and happy, exuberant songs. *Good-bye to Ur! Good-bye to Sumer!* Terah's caravan was on its way. And the sickle of a new moon hung low in the evening sky.

Day by day, the outline of Ur's *ziggurat,* across the plains behind them, grew faint and faded until "the House of the Great Light" was lost to sight; but, night by night, the crescent of that bright new moon increased in size to "show the way" for Terah's venture.

Now, for us, the fictitious boy in Ur, who might have been Abraham, can become the more historical figure, for with the migration from Ur Abraham's story may be said to begin. The best part of four thousand years has gone by since that day, yet the story is still told and retold year after year.

As the ancestor of their three great faiths, three great religions, the Jewish, Christian, and Islamic, cherish his name. He was *Abram* to the early Hebrews, *Abraham* to Jews and Christians, *Ibrahim* to the Moslems, the followers of Mohammed. He is called "the Father of the Faithful," "the Friend of God," and his name, around the world, to hundreds of millions of people[38] is still a symbol of leadership and faith.

It was in Ur (or Urfa), they say, that Abraham and his two brothers grew up and married, and here one of his brothers died leaving a son named *Lot*. There was Abraham and his wife, *Sarah*, and his nephew, Lot; and there was Terah, Abraham's father, and *Nahor*, Abraham's older brother, and Nahor's wife. But, it is to Abraham, above all, that the long tradition clings.

Whether his birthplace be located in the southern Sumerian delta — in *"Ur* of the Chaldees"[39] — as Genesis suggests, or in northern Mesopotamia — in "the *land* of the Chaldees" — as some scholars now have good reason to believe,[40] the pattern of his life is essentially the same. Sumerian and Akkadian (Semitic) and *Hurrian*[41] beliefs and customs and traditions surrounded him in either case — those he inherited and those he helped to perpetuate. And these beliefs, customs, and traditions, from records excavated in the Middle East in recent years, can now be presented with a growing measure of accuracy.

Terah took Abraham his son, and Lot . . . his son's son, and Sarah . . . his son Abraham's wife; and they went forth with them from Ur of the Chaldees, to go into the land of Canaan; and they came unto Harran, and dwelt there. . . . AND TERAH DIED IN HARRAN.[42]

10

Abraham's "People"

For us, with our ready reckoning of the natural seasons, the shortening days of autumn hold no fear. But for the earliest people of Harran, closely dependent as their lives had been upon the sun to maintain the fruitfulness of the earth and to assure the harvests by which they lived, the annual withdrawal of the sun's light and heat had held terror we cannot imagine.

The life cycle of the moon consumed a month, and then a new moon was "born." The life cycle of the sun's light consumed many months and the very slowness of its mysterious decline, as winter approached, had only intensified men's fears. They watched each day grow shorter than the last, each night grow longer and colder. They saw leaves wither and fall dead upon the ground, streams yield to the conquering grip of frost and ice, and plants blacken and die. Where would it end? they had asked. What if, this time, no power should stop the sun's descent? Then the light would continue to diminish and mankind would perish in a blacked-out world.

Year after year, in Abraham's time, in an annual festival, the people of Harran repeated the primitive rituals by which their ancestors had tried to sustain the dying sun's powers and "save the day." But to no immediate effect had their ancestors struggled. Daily, minute by minute, the daylight had continued to shorten. Finally, just as their terror was greatest and their ritual had become a losing frenzy, and it appeared their rites had been of no avail, there came the turning point, "the saving day" when the sun "stood still."

This was the solstice, the "Standing Still." This was the turning point: now, daily, the light and heat would increase. Now the wailing women of Harran who, six months before, had started their ritual of mourning for the sun-god's decline and continued it all through the shortening days of his descent into darkness, need mourn no more. This was the *Birthday of the*

Sun! they said. Each year on this day, the people of Harran came out of their dark, damp houses and the land rang with jubilation. It was a festival Terah's family knew well, and it has continued, in one form or another, into modern times in Syria and Egypt.

Sometimes, on the eve of the solstice, some of the celebrants withdrew into inner shrines or caves in Harran, from which at midnight they came forth loudly praising her whom the Semites called "the Heavenly Virgin" or "the Goddess of Heaven" and crying "The Virgin has brought forth. The light is waxing. The New Year is born!" Then for twelve days ceremonial bonfires brightened the nights in the people's symbolic effort to help the newly born sun rekindle its all but extinguished light and warmth. It was a festival of lights: it was *a turning point and a beginning* in Nature's cycle. It was the great and crowning festival of the Mesopotamian year, this "Standing Still" as they called it, when the day's light and heat triumphed over the night's darkness and cold, and Nature's New Year began.[43]

What the eve of the great "Standing Still" — the solstice — was to the natural world and to the people of northwestern Mesopotamia, Terah's death was to his son Abraham — *a turning point and a beginning* in Abraham's life. For at that moment Abraham stood between two traditions: the faith that had led his father and his own, as yet untried, convictions.

The pattern of his life in Harran had not differed much from his life in Ur except for the fact that there were numerous kinsmen living in surrounding towns and that Harran was a prosperous, growing city, ruled by an Amorite (Semitic) prince. Through Harran, in northwestern Mesopotamia, passed the main arteries of travel, east and west. If Terah had been a trader, as men have often supposed, in this northern city he would have had access to many markets denied him in Ur. Most of the gods, however, were the same, for An, Enlil, and Inanna and the rest of that pantheon were revered all over Mesopotamia, and both cities were centers of moon-god worship: only the name of the moon-god was different in Harran. Yet, with Terah's death, everything changed for Abraham.

At twilight one night, alone, on a slope high above the city of Harran, Abraham faced the new situation. All Terah's trusting people were his people now. Their flocks and herds were his. Their problems were his. Their successes and failures depended, in large measure, upon him. The yoke of his responsibilities sat more heavily on his shoulders than he had expected.

The night was calm. The sweep of landscape that fell away to the west drained with it the petty problems that had vexed his day. On his left hand lay the city; on his right, the mountains he had learned to love. Their purple shadows already filled the distant valleys but could not dim the inspiration and quiet sense of confidence the mountains gave him.

Abraham was about to forge new links in that chain of circumstances that was his family's life, and he knew it; yet, even as his fingers tightened on the bellows that would fire his plans, he could not quite forget the past. Pictures of his early home and childhood, like patterns in a kaleidoscope, passed before him in memory.

He saw Ur's *ziggurat* and Ur's festivals and her processions honoring the moon-god. He saw Terah the father teaching his children the religious traditions of his time; Terah the priest, sacrificing at the intimate, family altar of their home; Terah the head of his "people," keeping the family records; and, finally, Terah the law-maker, announcing the all-important decision to set out for Harran. But already the colors of the glass were softening and the pictures were not as sharp as once they might have been.

Terah was dead; and below Abraham lay just such a busy city, with its noisy markets and its many temples, as Ur had been. It was a city of Terah's choosing, under a god of Terah's choice. There, over the years of his father's leadership, the family had become well settled. They lived within easy distances of communication with numerous kinsmen who were also well established in the Balikh valley. Below him, in the city, lay a pattern of life that had become a routine; but it was not Abraham's pattern. In front of him spread the roads that led to the west — even to the Great Sea, men said — and to new opportunities.

He would be leaving the moon-god behind, if he left Harran, and many lesser gods as well. Did he really need them? True, each city had its divine protector, named and worshiped with pomp and pageantry. Each family had its god, so intimate as to be nameless, worshiped with simplicity as befitted a member of a family or tribe. Could it not be that, besides all these, each person also had his god, so much more personal that not only could the god be nameless, but his service might even be unspoken except in one man's heart? Abraham remembered An and Enlil and Inanna, yet all of these, at best, he thought, were pale and wan when compared to the mysterious, all-embracing divinity he sensed in the expansiveness of the heavens.

Abraham looked up into the lights of the first stars of evening and thought for a long, long time. What was it he wished for this "family" which now was his? "Abraham's people," that was what he desired his family to become — a unit that, under his leadership, would grow numerous and strong; a "people" whose good works would benefit mankind; a "name," honored by all who heard it, that for all generations would mark his family and his descendants as *Abraham's people!*

For all this, he needed a new country. Everything he had heard of Canaan drew him westward. Yet Abraham knew that to transplant Terah's happily settled family from Harran into a new and unknown soil might be to risk the very life and growth of the people he was now dedicated to serve. Perhaps — as with his choice of seed-times and harvests — it was the position of the stars that should guide his decision; that is what his neighbors believed.

. . . Abram arose and sat in the night at the new moon of the seventh month, so that he might observe the stars from the evening to the morning, so that he might know what would be the character of the year with regard to the rains, and he was sitting alone and observing.

And a word came into his heart and he said: "All the signs of the stars and the signs of the sun and of the moon are all in the hand of the Lord: why do I search them out?

"If He desires, he causes it to rain, morning and evening . . . and all things are in his hands."

And he prayed in that night, and said: "My God, God Most High, thou alone art a God to me, and thou hast created all things, and all things that are are the works of thy hand, and thee and thy god-ship have I chosen.

"Deliver me from the hands of the evil spirits who reign over the thoughts of the hearts of men, and let them not lead me astray from thee, my God. . . ." [44]

Under the open sky, now black with night, Abraham's senses reached out to claim the power God gives to every man. He felt less dependent upon the moon and stars and shrines and images, as his pulses swelled to meet that all-enveloping strength. He was overwhelmed by the weight of his desire to leave the city's hubbub and haggling and, trusting that unseen force, to live his own life, come what might, independent of its confusions. He remembered An, the good shepherd, leading "An's flocks." He, too, could be a "good shepherd" and his family a great people under his leadership. Again he felt strength swelling within him. As if a voice had spoken, it directed his decision.

"Get thee out of thy country, and from thy kindred, and from thy father's house, unto a land that I will show thee. And I will make of thee a great nation, and I will bless thee, and make thy name great. . . . And I will bless them that bless thee, and curse him that curseth thee: and in thee shall all families of the earth be blessed." [45]

Abraham needed only to recognize the unseen power and to trust that inner voice directing him.

And Abraham took Sarah his wife, and Lot his brother's son, and all their substance that they had gathered, and the souls they had gotten in Harran; and they went forth to go into the land of Canaan. . . . [46]

11

"To Go Into the Land of Canaan"

Again the planning, the packing, and the preparations for a long journey were under way. Again the eyes of youth looked forward with enthusiasm while those of age lingered on the now familiar environment and pattern of life in Harran.

And what of the trip? What were its difficulties, its excitements, its surprises and satisfactions? For there were difficulties. There were excitements. This journey was no story-book idyl: a trek from Harran to Canaan in the early second millennium B.C.E. was not an easy trip, nor was it accomplished without moments of danger and discouragement. The roads were not yet the highways of later years, made to accommodate chariots and other wheeled vehicles. They were rough, narrow, and treacherous. They were the caravan routes of adventurous traders.

Abraham had no horses or camels. Asses were his beasts of burden. Now they carried tents and blankets, tools and utensils, Sarah's harp and Sarah's loom, or even Sarah herself. Now the rhythm of their sharp little hoofs joggled a servant's sleepy children between bulging saddlebags and, for good measure, perhaps a lamb too young to keep up with the procession.

Out of Harran, due south, the route followed the valley of the Balikh River where, at Nahor, there were Aramaean relatives to entertain the travelers and speed them on their way. When the Balikh River joined the Euphrates and flowed east, the caravan crossed the river and continued south on the road to Tadmor. We can picture their progress, in imagination. The river's crossing would have been made with more excitement than damage and, after a few days' grazing beside the river, Abraham's caravan would have continued its unwieldy way.

Now the road skirted the wilderness, a rugged path which rose from the river valley into mountainous country, then dipped into verdant valleys where animals could forage and travelers set up camp, with a chance to bake their bread and wash their clothes and repair their tools and weapons.

Day by day, the journey continued. Only occasionally was the road broken by small settlements. On the left hand spread the fringe of the Arabian desert, sparsely dotted with isolated groups of huts or circles of nomads' tents; on the right were rocky mountain ranges, alive with wild game and studded now and then with habitable caves. Often, when not already locally occupied, these caves offered welcome shelter to travelers, but they could also conceal an ambushing party, raiding being not infrequent between Harran and the Mediterranean coast.

Let us imagine Abraham and his caravan camping for a few days a hundred miles or more east of the city of Damascus. They had been caught in a spell of bad weather and taken shelter, some in their own waterproof goats' hair cloth tents and some in a nearby cave. When the bad weather lifted, Abraham had lingered for a few more days in order to allow the sun to dry up some of the deep mud that would impede their way — only for a few days, however, since the crescent of a new month's moon gave promise of good traveling.

The tents and blankets had finally been packed. The family was cleaning up from its last meal and some of the cooking pots had already been hung behind the saddlebags for the animals to carry, when a string of heavily laden asses and six men came into sight.

It was Lot who first saw the men, leading their animals to the water hole whose location seemed not unfamiliar to them. Lot greeted the travelers with respect and brought them to Abraham, who immediately ordered that food and drink be brought for his guests.

There was confusion and consternation among the cooks, who were in the midst of disposing of whatever remained from their recent meal. But the fire was not yet out, and they added several measures of milk to the remains of the soup they had had for lunch, still bubbling in its copper kettle. There was plenty of bread, newly baked in anticipation of resuming their journey, and cheese which, although already packed in a half-filled bag, could be retrieved without delay. So bread and cheese and milk soup were brought and the men ate greedily.

They were uncouth fellows, sulky and disheveled, and they warmed very little to Abraham's hospitality. Nomad law required that Abraham ask no questions until the men had been fed. It also stipulated that, having eaten his food, the guests could not harm the host.

When the meal was over, instead of reclining for a friendly chat, as was customary, the newcomers showed great curiosity as to Abraham's caravan and a restlessness that led them to wander in and out among the cargo as it was being packed. The strangers could see for themselves that Abraham's possessions were no mean accumulation.

Was their host a trader? they asked, in a *patois* one of Abraham's servants found easy to translate.

No.

Was he en route to Damascus?

Yes.

Was he a rich man?

With Oriental modesty, Abraham pointed to the meager meal he had been able to supply. The men continued their questions.

Had Abraham come from Kanish?

No, only from Harran.

Was the road patrolled?

Abraham had seen no government agents.

Did Abraham have silver in his possessions?

The question was blunt, the implication sharp. Their host became suspicious. He would parry such thrusts with evasions.

Silver? Where would he get the means to buy silver, with so many mouths to feed? Abraham indicated his surrounding family, some of whom were busily packing and some standing around in little knots waiting for the strangers to depart. And how could a poor man whose family required so many tents and blankets and utensils and so much foodstuff be burdened with such a heavy cargo as silver, even if it were *given* to him?

The men were in too much of a hurry to argue the point. They appraised their position: they had been fed; their animals had had water and a rest; they had filled their water bottles; before Abraham might turn the tables and start asking questions that might be embarrassing to them, they had better be on their way. One final request: Did Abraham, this gracious chieftain, this host without equal, have any sweet-smelling balm and a loaf of moldy bread he could spare his unworthy guests for their injured companion?

Companion? Where? Everyone looked around. And there the poor man was, his half-conscious body and an empty water bag draped over the saddlebags of one of the asses.

Abraham offered to wash and dress the man's wounds and give him nursing care. His companions were indifferent and impatient. They would attend to him later, they said. When Lot spoke up and asked what had happened, the men were evasive. Pressed by Abraham, however, they were at no loss for an answer: the clumsy fellow, that blockhead, had fallen over a rock he had not seen in his path and bumped his head and barked his shin.

Was that all?

That was all. The men lied; actually the fellow was badly hurt. Abraham and Lot did not believe their story.

With an elaborate gesture of *farewell,* and little or no thanks for the bread and the pot of scented balm one of the servants brought forward, the men and their heavily laden animals staggered away in the direction of Tadmor.

There was little time then to discuss Abraham's strange visitors if the caravan was to be off in the light of the new moon's waxing, but their visit furnished unending gossip and conjecture as the caravan made its way along the road to Damascus. Late the next day, on a deeply wooded stretch of road, Abraham's family came upon its sequel.

Again it was Lot who noticed the first evidence: beside the road there were two graves, freshly dug and heaped with stones to keep the wolves away. In a nearby cave four men nursed a badly injured, older man and a servant with a bandaged head. These had been the victims of Abraham's surly visitors with their heavily laden pack animals and their half-conscious, neglected companion.

The men in the cave were Damascene traders and of one family. They had been returning from Kanish with a cargo

which included precious silver to be sold to silversmiths in
Damascus. Being a small group themselves, they had traveled,
for safety's sake, with another small group of friendly merchants
that they had met en route. At Tadmor, the others had turned
west: they were taking their silver to northern cities of the
Mediterranean coast for sale and export. From Tadmor, therefore, the Damascenes had had to travel alone, eight of them,
well armed, and with a fine load of merchandise.

Here, in this cave, the brigands had lain in wait for the
first promising cargo that would go by. The weather had put
the Damascenes off their guard and in one foolish moment of
relaxation — trudging, single file, and singing at the top of
their voices as they approached a little defile which framed
the first sunset they had seen in many days — in that one
moment, they had walked into a trap.

Now, two of the brothers were dead, their father was out
of his mind with shock, and one of their bravest servants was
bruised and bandaged and, as yet, unable to get about. Their
animals were gone, their cargo stolen, and even their commonest belongings scattered and lost.

Among Abraham's people, there was no lack of sympathy
and assistance for these poor travelers, whose plight, they
realized, might have been their own. They vied with one
another in their efforts to feed, clothe, and encourage the suf-
ferers. They rearranged their own dunnage so that the injured
men could have mounts. Then they moved out of the defile
into more open country and set up a camp site where the men
could rest and recuperate before the two families, together,
headed once more for Damascus.

Abraham, eager to be off, yet content to wait until his new
friends would be able to withstand the trip, had time to ponder
many things. What made men into predatory beasts, he wondered; killing and maiming and stealing, when they could be
brothers, enjoying the fruits of the earth together and sharing
the work of their hands? He could answer his own question
no more than he could explain what made a pair of lions constant unto death and the coo-coo bird an indifferent mother.

No two alike, no two the same.

And soon the caravan proceeded on its way toward Canaan.

12

Sarah

Sarah was tired and cross. Sarah had been cross before, and tired. In fact, often the two went together. The confusions of the last few days had borne heavily on Abraham's wife, and the addition of the extra travelers, with little or no food of their own and minus their own pack animals, and with two of the men injured to boot, had demanded her attention. On top of that, it was discovered that the cloth she had spread to bleach in the dew, two nights before, had been forgotten and left behind.

It was to have been a tunic for Abraham, white linen woven with stripes of bright color — an intricate task for which she had dyed the colors herself. Now the flax and the dyes had been gathered to no purpose; the spinning, too, had been wasted; and her own long hours of weaving had gone for nought. All this, because some addlepated servant had the memory of a nit!

In vain had Eliezer, the steward, promised that he would send swift messengers to retrace their route and retrieve the precious cloth. In vain had the imperious Sarah forbidden him to delay Abraham's passage further. But he had sent the men just the same, without telling her. Eliezer knew Sarah. It would be many a day before any of them would be allowed to forget the incident if the linen were not recovered. Already the runners had been gone twelve hours. With good fortune, they could return by daybreak.

Abraham loved Sarah. When she was sharp-tongued, impatient, testy, still he loved her. These were but surface outbursts, not the true Sarah, he told himself. He learned to treat them as such and turn deaf at a moment's notice. When that failed, he had another device: he went out of doors and about his business until the fires that crackled so hot within her had burned themselves out.

Abraham never ceased to love Sarah. He knew the great unspoken sorrow of her heart, because he shared it — the lack of children of their own. Long years he had measured her moods.

He had noted the hostility which, gradually, had crept into her speech whenever the parenthood of others became too much for her to bear, and he remembered how that hostility had melted, and the goodness of her heart shone through, following his brother Haran's tragic death. He had seen his wife bend over the widowed mother to comfort her, one arm across the fatherless Lot's shoulders also. Then her guard was down and all the sweetness of character that Abraham had so loved in her youth rose to the surface with her words of consolation.

He remembered her as a girl, his bride, in Ur. Who could recall as well as he the grace with which she balanced the two-handled water jug on her young shoulder, coming to and from the well; the dignity with which she received the family's guests though little more than a child herself; the earnestness with which she attended the sacrificial rites? He remembered how joyously she had helped to celebrate the spring-planting festivals, and how sorrowfully the harvest rites that filled her empty arms with corn and fruits but never gave her the baby for which she longed.

He remembered, too, her temper. It had not always been so sharp. At first it had been only a bright blade flashing, and he had loved the unexpected thrusts of her keen mind. Then it had become more of a shield than a sword, a defense that covered the disappointment of her childlessness. And, finally, when Time had worn both shield and sword to a thin and ragged edge, it became a self-inflicting weapon whose piercing edge she scarcely realized.

Were the vicissitudes of the trip to Canaan going to prove too much for Sarah to bear? Abraham asked himself. Had he erred in taking her away from a home that was a well-appointed house and from the relatively comfortable living they had enjoyed in the city of Harran? Or was it only in fatigue that her speech was more cutting than usual?

During their years in Harran with Terah, how bounteously, how completely, Sarah and the steward, Eliezer, had cared for the ever-growing family of relatives, servants, and slaves. They saw to it that there was always on hand wool for the weavers, clay for the potters, hides for the sandal-makers, flour for the cooks, and curds for the cheese-makers, paying out the raw materials with one hand while the other received back the clothes and shoes and blankets and utensils and food for one and all. Now their efforts must be many times more complicated in order to keep up with the needs of the family while on the road.

Eliezer would have his reward. In the absence of children of his own, Abraham had made Eliezer his heir, as was commonly done under the ancient laws of those lands. But would Sarah ever have the reward she craved — children of her own to bring up, like other women?

Next morning the messengers returned. They brought the cloth to Eliezer, and even some honeycomb they had collected on the way. Together, they found Sarah just outside her tent, feeding and playing with a young lamb whose injured foot she had just bandaged. As she wiped the salve from her capable fingers, she was laughing like a child at the playful lamb's three-legged antics.

It was hard for the haughty Sarah to say, *Thank you.* Her gratitude to Eliezer and his messengers was meager to say the least. Relieved as she was to have the linen back, pleased as she was with the honey, and indebted as she was to Eliezer, she accepted the linen and the honeycomb with little more than a lift of her chin. Was she abashed, chagrined, or ashamed? Who could say?

The fires of the day before were out, but, when the men had left, she turned to Abraham inside the tent with one last, little sputtering spark; "Eliezer did not mind me. Tell him to mind me, Abraham. Tell him *I will be minded.*"

13

Mount of the Amorite

Abraham's family lingered briefly in Damascus, the men and women alike loath to leave the fascination of its markets. For Damascus was a unique outpost on the desert frontier. It was an oasis rich in fresh water and abundant food; and famous for the high quality of its craftsmen's products. Its prosperity stemmed from the fact that the great, snow-capped mountains that crowned its northern background watered and made fertile the valleys of the land. Like the city of Harran, it spread its name and influence over a far greater area than the immediate environs of the city itself.

Out of Damascus the route reverted to a wilderness road, broken only infrequently by small settlements. On the one hand lay the fringe of habitable, but sparsely settled, desert; on the other, the mountains with their occasional caves.

Now the travelers were under the shadow of snow-capped Mt. Hermon. Now they were passing through Hobah and Dan, and thence down the river valley to Canaanite Hazor, little dreaming that any of the villages and isolated way stations through which they passed would become, in time, cities that history would record.

Finally, the country became increasingly less craggy and the climate somewhat milder. There were fewer caves. There were houses made of rough, grey limestone. Following the ancient trade route known as "the way of the sea," they crossed the Jordan River below Lake Huleh and found themselves on the fertile plains which lay northwest of the Sea of Galilee. They were at last in the land of Canaan.[47]

It was good to come upon rolling, tillable land and to breathe the gentle fragrance of the soil. It was good to find fig trees growing heavy with the sweet burden of their fruit and to see olives ripening among the shimmering, silvery leaves that crowned the gnarled and twisted tree trunks.

More exciting than the land, the stone houses, or the vegetation, however, more welcome even than the sight of the Sea of Galilee and its fishing, was an ancient, moon-god city which awaited just such weary travelers as they, at the southern end of the Sea of Galilee.[48] *Beth-yerah* ("House of the Moon"), it was called; and it mattered only a little that its temple was, even then, old and battered and neglected, and in danger of becoming a ruin. To Abraham and his people, it brought back memories of Terah and Ur and Harran.

Soon, Mt. Tabor was behind them, its valley warm to their feet. Then, at last, before the happy travelers' eyes there appeared the wide, fertile, well-watered plain of beautiful Esdraelon, which stretches east and west from Mt. Gilboa to Mt. Carmel, with a pass to the Great Sea. From an altitude of more than two thousand feet at Damascus, they had descended to a valley little more than two hundred feet above sea level.

It was good to be able to let the animals graze again in open country, good to set up their tents in the form of a wide, three-quarters' circle and enjoy a few days' rest and recuperation.

Abraham's family spread its belongings within the circle of tents and unpacked a few of the sacks. The women washed their clothes at a nearby spring and hung them to dry on an old stone wall halfway up the hill above the spring. The men sharpened and repaired their tools, cared for the animals, hunted, explored, and traded, while the women cooked and washed and gossiped.

Two women at a time ground grain between stones. Others pounded it into a coarse flour in stone mortars. They added water and leaven, let the dough rise, and then shaped it into loaves for baking. Usually there was meat only on special days or when a sacrifice was in order: soon a lamb was roasting over the fire. Its fat melted and dripped into the fire, sending out hissing spits of flame and meaty, tempting odors. A primitive churn was set up. It was made of a tripod of sticks with a goat's skin full of milk slung between the three sticks in such a way that a woman could sit and shake the wobbly, skin vessel until the butter "came."

For the evening meal there were hot cakes baked on

heated stones as well as crusty bread fresh from the oven. There was honey from a hive of wild bees they had come upon a few days before. And if they could interest some Canaanite in a trade for some of the healing balm and resinous gum they had brought with them, there might be cucumbers as well, and even melons.

Soon they would hear the valley echo to the songs and shouts of merriment in the vineyards in the hills above them, where grape-treaders, barefooted, would dance in Canaan's large, stone wine vats. Already the songs of Canaan were stirring the newcomers' blood. They, too, felt the urge to sing and dance and shout, to laugh and rejoice. In this new country, much that was strange encircled them, but Abraham's family was disposed to like Canaan. Among the older people, who twice had left established homes and friendly faces to follow Terah and Abraham, there were some who were homesick, but when night came and the familiar stars and moon appeared above them, Canaan was no longer a strange land.

For Abraham, it was enough to scan the beautiful valley rising in wide and colorful slopes to the pass of Megiddo and to Carmel surmounting the sea, and to realize that the long trek from Ur to Harran and from Harran to Canaan was over. Now, to wander from one slope of good pasture to another and from one spring of water to another well, to settle for a few months or a few years in one location and move again whenever he so desired was to be his life. In Canaan's out-of-doors he would be as much at home as he had ever been in any house in Ur or Harran.

He saw the clusters of Canaanite houses that, here and there, indicated settlements across the plain and turned back with pride and satisfaction to his own circle of black tents. In a few weeks, by easy stages, the caravan would climb again, this time into the more sparsely settled hills of central Canaan, the so-called *Mount of the Amorite* that was to become his family's particular homeland.

Here they would settle down for a time in some location where there would be pastures and water and food sufficient for their needs. They would set up their ovens and churns and dye pots, and assemble their looms. Here the sheep could be sheared, the wool carded and spun, and cloth woven. The potter could turn his wheel and renew their supply of cooking pots and storage jars. And the animals could graze and rest.

Yes, it was good to be in Canaan at last.

What did the Canaanites think of this caravan of foreigners that spread itself, without so much as a by-your-leave, over Canaan's slopes and plains? Little or nothing. The people of Canaan were used to the appearance, seasonally, of just such *'Apiru* ("wanderers") who, year by year, came seeking food and pasturage in Canaan, sometimes as raiders from the desert but more often in peaceful guise.

It was the foreigners who asked the questions.

What were these strange tales they heard concerning Canaan's *Lord of the Earth?* And what of these shrines, these "high places," they had passed on their way into Canaan?

14

Canaan

Canaan was the most western of all the "land of the Amorite." In its earliest years, it had been settled, and its population often renewed, largely by nomads from the Arabian Desert who, little by little, over the years, succumbed to a sedentary life. They found the character of the land — little pockets of hills and fertile valleys surrounded by craggy barriers — well suited to men who had been accustomed to living in small, isolated clans in the desert. These nomad families established themselves very comfortably in Canaan. They lived in isolated centers which grew into cities over each of which one man, its chieftain or patriarch, became leader, or "prince," and priest and lawgiver. Most, but not all, of such centers were in the lowlands, the hill country being more generally pasture land.

As he first explored Canaan's plains and ranged her fertile hillsides, the primitive desert-born nomad had marveled at what he saw. How the moist earth gave of its nourishment for its earth-children! How it stored water for their thirsty green mouths! How it sheltered its fragile plants and made vigorous its bolder specimens! Roots, some growing as large as the trunk of a good-sized tree, and others as delicate as a thread of flax — and all of them alive! He observed how the earth provided the needed environment for all: crags for the eagles' nests, fir trees for the storks'; leaves under the snow for the hepaticas, lush marshes for the lilies, swift water for the cress! All this was new to the desert-born.

He had come from the dry and almost treeless desert where all was still and sparse into a land of green hills, fertile valleys, and abundant water. The silence of the desert is constant, its monotony endless. It breeds men of endurance but offers little stimulus to expansion of thought. But in Canaan, the sound of the trees' foliage shaken by the wind, the chatter of running water or the clatter of rolling stones loosed by a sudden freshet; the forests; the mysteries of the rain, the dew, and the frost — and all the other confusions of sound and sight in that fertile, rain-blessed country — quickened the no-mads' imagination and made plausible the idea of an unseen Owner or Master who ruled the earth.

The early Canaanite roamed the mountains and knew something of their hidden bounties. It was not that the moun-tain peak brought him nearer to God, or offered a staircase by which his god could descend to him, as with the Sumerians, but that within the mountain he recognized a mysterious energy.

There had been mystery, too, in Canaan's rocks and caves. Both the rock and the cave were secure. They resisted storms and stress and survived the greatest calamities, unmoved and unchanged. In the desert, they offered shade on a long march; in Canaan, they provided shelter from the devastating, death-dealing east wind. Surely, thought the early Canaanites, only some invisible Lord of the earth is able to maintain such strength unmoved: the spirit of the Lord must dwell in the rock; it must be, in fact, his home.

Water was a living thing to the nomad. He saw it move. He heard it "chatter." Even to taste it brought life-giving in-vigoration. And if he drained a water-hole, did not the water immediately renew itself? If, at the brook, he held the water back, did it not struggle into a new path, and so away from him? It had life, spirit, he thought.

The tree, too, had life, spirit. Neither man nor animal could replace a lost limb, but cut off a bough of a tree, and the tree sent out new growth to take its place!

Beyond a man's ownership of a field or spring or tree or cave, Canaan's earliest settlers had recognized a greater Owner and Master. This was the Canaanite's *Baal*, his Lord of the earth, the storm, and the heavens. As there were many springs and trees and heights and rocks, so there were many places where the Lord of the earth was "recognized."

When a man came upon a scene of exceptional beauty or strength — a waterfall, a giant oak, a sheltering peak, or a protecting cave — or when a terrifying thunder storm, an earth tremor or some other natural event baffled his understanding,

The Canaanite Baal about to hurl his thunderbolts: a stela (2000-1800 B.C.E.) found at Ugarit where, having stood under an open skylight in the Temple of Baal, its surface was worn by the rain of centuries (time of Abraham).

he was conscious — as the early Mesopotamian had been conscious — of the great, unseen forces that surrounded him, and he cried out, "Surely the Lord is in this place ! His presence makes it holy." And there he built *an altar to the Lord*.

Thus there had grown up in Canaan, from very early times, sanctuaries and shrines, and even temples, where the Lord was propitiated, singly or by a community of worshipers.

All over Canaan, archaeologists have found such ancient shrines with evidence of ceremonies and offerings. And they have found, while excavating old Canaanite cities, in the ruins of temples and other ancient buildings, tablets inscribed with early hymns and rituals and religious myths sacred to *Baal, Lord of all.*[49]

The Canaan of the nomadic settler, however picturesque, was not quite the Canaan of Abraham's day. The mystery of Canaan's mountains, streams, and vegetation continued and the reverence of the Lord of the earth and storm survived, but the isolated settlements became, in time, a group of bustling cities.

As early as the fourth millennium B.C.E., there had been cities in Canaan; in the third, a peak in their cultural history had been reached. So when Abraham's caravan arrived in the early second millennium, Canaan was an old and settled country with a high level of commercial, cultural, and artistic achievement. Yet, until a few decades ago, our knowledge of the country and its people was as meager as our grandparents' and limited, almost entirely, to Biblical references. Mistakenly, we had pictured the Canaanites as being as primitive and as nature-bound as their nomadic forebears. And knowing nothing of Canaan's commerce, we knew next to nothing about the neighboring countries with whom Canaan had trade relations.

Where, then, did scholars come upon the wider information?

It was in 1928, in our own day, that a Syrian peasant was ploughing his field on a hillside near the town of *Ras Shamra* on the Syrian coast. Below him, westward, lay a little harbor of the Mediterranean Sea. Imagine the peasant's surprise when, suddenly, the blade of his plough struck a large, cut stone which

Images from Ugarit (XIV-XIII century B.C.E.), showing long-bearded men who look more Sumerian that Semitic, and a chariot (restored).

led to the discovery that underneath his farm lay a fine burial chamber which had been built, several thousand years earlier, outside an ancient city which turned out to be the old city of *Ugarit*.

Ugarit, *a few centuries after Abraham*, had been an important seaport, connecting Harran and all Mesopotamia, and settlements all the way to the Indus valley perhaps, with Canaan and Egypt and the "islands of the sea." Although the name, Ugarit, had been deciphered on Babylonian tablets in 1907, the location and importance of the city had been unknown, and its identification with Ras Shamra unsuspected, until the peasant's discovery.

Since then, in Ugarit, not only ruins of temples and other buildings have been brought to light, but a library of cuneiform tablets has been found which furnishes texts and documents — many of them later than Abraham's time but others, copies of texts and songs and rituals in use since long before his day. They are written in two languages[50] — one, an archaic Canaanite dialect closely related to early Hebrew and Phoenician; the other, a Hurrian dialect; the Hurrians (north and east of the Tigris area) being an important people wholly unknown a generation ago.[51]

From the "finds" at Ugarit, we learn that Canaan's cities were old and sophisticated in Abraham's day; that in art and music Canaan excelled her neighbors, her bronze work alone at that time being famous from the Indus to "the islands." We discover, too, how closely Canaan's gods, from earliest times, had been associated with planting and harvesting and the turn of the seasons, and learn something about Canaanite festivals. Among the texts are copies of epic poems and myths, rituals and songs much older than the city itself. Some of them are unique, and some suggestive of those of other countries with which, it now turns out, the seaport city of Ugarit had extensive cultural and trade relations.

At *Mari*,[52] the ancient Amorite capital on the middle Euphrates, excavations made since 1933 have also been rich in historical and religious texts. Some of the documents deal with diplomatic affairs, some with metal-working and other sources of industry. There are official communications and commercial agreements, here and in Ugarit, which show that these people were in close touch with Ugarit and other Mediterranean cities. Yet we had pictured the Canaanites as primitive and provincial!

Again at *Nuzi* (*Nuzu*),[53] east of the Tigris River, recent excavations have found evidence of another ancient people, the Hurrians, who also had business and cultural relations as far westward as the Mediterranean Sea. They, too, have left religious and legal texts of real importance to our understanding of the people through whose lands Abraham's caravan traveled.

There have been other productive "finds" since 1920, as well as discoveries before that date. But the excavations at Ras Shamra (Ugarit), Mari, and Nuzi, especially, have changed and enlarged our whole picture of "the land of the Amorite," and made possible a new understanding of Canaan, before, during, and after Abraham's time.

15

The "High Place" of Shechem

In Canaan Abraham and his family were not quite the city dwellers they had been in Ur and Harran. Neither were they nomads. They lived within close range of the safety of Canaan's cities and, like their neighbors, sent their herds and flocks for pastureage to the nearby hills and valleys. They were semi-nomads: dependent upon pasturage to feed their animals, and upon crops to supply their grain and vegetables. But they were free to move about, since they were not tied to the land by fruit-growing as were the more settled Canaanite farmers. Yet they, too, must, in time, become farmers in Canaan.

They had much to learn.

They must become accustomed to the continual dampness of Canaan's cold, rainy winters; to the devastating blows of the cruel east wind; to the contrasts of parching heat and bitter frost which their shepherds would have to endure; to the hazards of drought and dry water holes. There were compensating surprises, however, in the fact that Canaan had two rainy seasons; in the cooling relief of the welcome northwest breeze that rolled in every summer afternoon from the Mediterranean Sea thirty miles away; in the heavy dew that, in normal summers, could be counted upon to irrigate their crops; and in the soft, night wind by which the Canaanite winnowed his grain.

Generally speaking, Canaan had only two seasons, winter and summer, cold and hot, wet and dry. Spring and fall were brief intervals at best.

When the summer was over, Abraham's people watched the Canaanite farmer pushing his wooden plough to turn the topsoil of his fields. He filled the folds of his tunic with grain and strode across his ploughed land, scattering the seeds with a wide, rhythmic gesture. Then he waited for the winter rains to begin.

When the cold, damp days of winter were gone, green

101

sprouts sprang up in the fields and buds of wild tulip and iris were weeds among the grain shoots. Suddenly, Abraham's family awoke one morning to find the whole, moist countryside had sprung into riotous life, each flowering slope as brilliant as a sunset, each cultivated field a pattern of bright green plants. Swallows nested in the blue-green cypress trees, disputing their possession with noisy sparrows. Quail sheltered their young in the hillsides' lush, new growth. The love-call of the turtledove was heard in the land, and baby lambs frisked in the welcome sunshine.

In a few, all-too-short weeks, this wondrous pageant of sight and sound was gone and the dry season had begun. Then each Canaanite would wend his way to some shrine and make his offering and his prayer, hoping that the great Lord of the Earth who knew how to hurl the thunderbolt and scatter the rain would show pity and send the second rainy season, lest the barley and wheat, the cucumbers and melons, the grapes and figs, wither and die.

It was this Lord of the earth who controlled the seasons and sent the wind and the rain, the Canaanites said. Sometimes, in their prayers, they called him *Baal,* sometimes *Hadad,* and sometimes they called him by other names — *Great Mountain,* for one — but always he was Lord of earth and storm and second only to a supreme, over-reaching, all-inclusive Canaanite deity called *the all-mighty El.* Often they would pray to El's wife, *Ashirat,* the Canaanite "bride of heaven," beseeching her to act for Baal or the Lord of all. Sometimes, they made a triad of their greatest gods: El, the all-father; El's wife, Ashirat; and Baal (Hadad) representing the son; with Baal the most active member of the trinity.[54]

Abraham soon observed that the Canaanites' places of worship were usually located at especially picturesque spots where it was easy to feel one's self in the presence of a divine spirit. These locations were often on heights of land. They were called "high places" and holy places. Sometimes it was beside an old, and beautiful, tree — perhaps an oak or a terebinth — that the worshipers made a pile of stones, or set up one large stone, as an altar on which to place their gifts. There they would listen to the wind as it twisted and swayed

The Canaanite Baal, a gold-plated bronze statuette (XV-XIV century B.C.E.) found at Ugarit. Canaan, even in Abraham's day, was famous for the quality of its bronze work.

the branches and made the leaves rustle and moan. The divine spirit was speaking, they said; and some wise priest would try to interpret the message. The petitioners would hang shreds of cloth from their garments on the leafy branches of the sacred tree, in order that their appeal might "touch" the unseen Lord.

Sometimes it was a spring that struggled and bubbled and "laughed" into which they would throw some possession. Sometimes it was a small plant that bled when its stem was broken that claimed their interest, and they felt in it an unseen life and spirit. Abraham often came upon altar stones pitted with holes, stained by the blood of sacrifices or by marks of the oil with which such altars were anointed.

In the high valley between Mount Ebal and Mount Gerizim, lay the already ancient city of *Shechem* (one of the few cities located in "the hill country"); and just outside the city wall, in a grove on the nearby "plain of Moreh," stood one of the most famous of all Canaan's sacred trees. It was called "the terebinth of Moreh" and "the terebinth of the diviners" (soothsayers).

Situated as Shechem was, at the crossroads where the main north-south road met the east-west road to the sea — the only real pass across the range — the princes of Shechem's city had entertained many a caravan and shared the plain of Moreh and Shechem's shrine with many a stranger before Abraham's family came to Canaan.

For generations, people had been coming to the "high place" at Shechem to petition the unseen Lord at the terebinth of Moreh. Again and again, while sheep grazed peacefully on hillsides surrounding the mountain and grapes turned blue in its vineyards, the valleys below rocked with the songs and shouts and frenzied appeals of the petitioners. At such times, smoke rose in billowing gusts above the altar and the meaty odors of an ass or a sheep roasting for the sacrifice filled the air.

And here, on the wide and sightly plain of Moreh, the prince of Shechem made Abraham and his family welcome to settle.

The breath-taking panorama from Mount Ebal was like

nothing Abraham had ever experienced before. Northward, in undulating peaks, it reached to the white snows of the Lebanons. To the west, fitfully, it fell away to the blue Mediterranean. Eastward, on eye level, it stretched to the lavender-greys of the misty horizon beyond the Jordan River gulch. And in between, under a pattern of shifting clouds, the peaks and valleys, and the sunshine and shadows, provided a vast palette of colors — muted, as were the feelings Abraham's words could not quite express. His spirits were high, and humble, as he drank in the beauty of the scene at this "holy place." This was the goal, he thought, towards which, unknowingly, he had climbed since childhood. Here, he "belonged."

Now that Abraham and his family were settled for an indefinite time in this inspiring place, they came to have the same kind of feeling about it that the Canaanites had. They, too, became responsive to the natural beauty around them. They, too, became sensitive to something unseen and unknown. They felt a sanctity in the "holy" tree and in the mystery of the mountains' enduring strength. The god to whom the people of Shechem prayed seemed like the god to whom Abraham had often prayed, and the family saw no harm — indeed, they saw hope — in making gifts at the Canaanites' altar and in listening to whatever the Shechemites' "gifted one," their "diviner," might be inspired to foretell.

For many months Abraham accepted Shechem's hospitality, shared Shechem's Canaanite festivals, listened to the priest interpret the sounds in the rustling, wind-swept foliage of the giant terebinth. He even erected his own altar for his own ceremonies, "an altar unto the Lord who appeared unto *him*." [55]

Sometimes while he stood beneath the holy tree, his prayers became very personal. The fearful thought that he had no son of his own spoke louder in his heart than all his other needs. Oh, that he might have a son to inherit, and descendants to enjoy, this wide and bounteous country he had chosen for his homeland!

Here, at the terebinth of Moreh, Abraham prayed that the Lord of the earth would bless and keep his people and give his

children, forever and ever, this gracious, fruitful land that
spread before his eyes. But only a faint answer came from the
rustling leaves of the "holy" tree.

Finally, the time came when the flocks needed fresh pastures. The circle of black tents was broken up, and Abraham
led his people across the hills to another camping site, not far
off and still on the Amorite Mountain, between the city of *Luz,*
later called Beth-el,[56] and the ruins of a still older city once
called *Ai.*[57] There, in a location almost as beautiful as Shechem,
Abraham established his family in a place he need share with
no other prince, his place; and there he set up a stone altar of
his own under another "holy" tree.

And Abraham saw, and behold, the land was pleasant and extended
and very wide, and everything grew on it, [grape] vines and figs
and pomegranates and terebinths and oil trees and cedars and
Lebanon trees and cypresses and all the trees of the field; and water
was upon the hills. And he blessed the Lord who had led him out
of Ur of the Chaldees and brought him to this hill. And . . . he
built an altar on this hill, and called upon the name of the Lord:
"Thou art my God, the God unto eternity." And he placed upon the
altar a sacrifice unto the Lord, that he should be with him and should
not desert him all the days of his life.[58]

When, again, the needs of food and pasturage and water
demanded a new location for the family, Abraham chose to
move southward. The tent pegs were pulled, the belongings
packed, and the altar Abraham had built at Luz was left behind; and soon the family's flocks were eating their way towards
the Negeb, "the South Country" of Canaan.

16

Threat of Famine

Not all at once does famine settle on a people. A series of years of none-too-plentiful harvests or some such catastrophe as a scourge of locusts must already have lowered the storage bins. The water shortage, too, must have become more than ordinarily acute, since drought is the mother of famine.

It is born with soft, undeveloped claws that do no more than test the temper of the situation, and mature only when famine grows callous and hard. Its warning cries measure and develop the resourcefulness of its victims and sometimes, mercifully, it is overcome before it is fully grown; and the people are well rid of it! But if it grows, it spreads and its claws deepen until it hugs the whole land in its cruel embrace.

Then famine tightens its grip like a wet knot shrinking.

Hunger and thirst stalk at its heels like twin progeny, but famine is indifferent to their cries. The sheep hang their heads together, abject, breathless in misery. Goats with swollen dugs no longer hurry to the milking women at night, nudging each other savagely, competing as to which shall be first to be milked. The water holes are parched. Vegetation lies sear upon the ground. The young stock grow languid and thin, the older cattle bony and gaunt. Cheese and butter are in short supply. The grain reserve dwindles, and neighbors are less and less willing to barter if it be food one comes to buy.

So it was, Abraham found, with famine in Canaan. Its approach was gradual, its misery progressive. There was nothing sharp and decisive about its blow — a crime gotten over with in haste: its striking power increases slowly; its death blow is heavy and long drawn-out. Yet there were signs of its coming for those who could read them.

After several years of unusually dry weather and poor harvests, there came a fall when the people of Canaan watched

107

in vain for the rain clouds from the southwest to roll in with
their usual density. They knew that without the moisture of
the winter rains, there was small chance of good harvests the
following year.

Meanwhile, the Canaanite farmers sowed their seed, still
hopeful that the Lord of the earth would not for too long
withhold the precious winter rains. But the winter rains were
light.

The Canaanite had seen winters with scanty rainfall before. He had learned to live through uncertain seasons. Abraham had had less experience with the vagaries of Canaan's
weather. He listened thoughtfully to his neighbors' misgivings
and predictions. It was the lack of spring rain, it appeared,
that would now be crucial. Soon, the winter was over and it
was spring.

Lilies splashed red upon the fields. Grape hyacinths
painted the hillsides blue, and odors of narcissus, hyacinth, and
cyclamen filled the air. The almond trees blossomed, and in
the bright promise their beauty displayed the farmers' fears re-
laxed somewhat. Who could despair when acacias, weighted
by their graceful sprays of yellow blossoms, spread like a
blessing from Ashirat above his head?

It was spring! The winter was over! The people came out
of their cold houses. It was a time to rejoice and enjoy the
sunshine, a time of singing birds and flowering hillsides and
joyous festivals. Now the stars hung like watchtowers across
the sky and in the soft radiance of the night men forgot that
it was not so much stars that lighted their fields as the slanting
rays of an ever-faithful, waning moon, low on the horizon.

In a wave of defiant promise, seeds sprouted feebly in the
valleys, but neither the barley nor the wheat was strong. Their
stands were thin and dry and less vigorous than the farmers
liked. Only the tares, those weeds that choke the young grain
and whose seeds make people ill — only the tares seemed inured
to the lack of winter moisture.

The time of spring's flowering was short and the spring
rains all too meager. In a matter of days, the brilliant colors
were gone, and the dry season had begun. In a matter of weeks,
the green that had been left upon the hills had changed to

brown, the brown to a monotonous grey, and the grey to a
persistent, straw-colored reflection of the sun. Then apprehen-
sion settled like a thin cloud upon the Canaanites. The level
of water in the village well fell. How long, wondered Abraham,
could they continue to fill the skin buckets which they let down
on an ever-lengthening rope?

Now Abraham leaned upon his faith in invisible powers,
and, with the Canaanites, he prayed that the Lord of the earth
would hurl his thunderbolts and bring the rain. Wholeheart-
edly, he and his family entered into the Canaanites' festivals of
propitiation.

As the days of drought continued, Sarah fingered more
tenderly the *teraphim* they had brought from Ur, and members
of her large family argued, each according to the customs of
his birthplace, what could be done to avert the hunger and
death Canaan's famine foretold.

Some of them believed that, in wandering so far from
Harran, the family had "lost touch" with the old gods that
really cared for them. There had been those in Abraham's caravan who, on leaving Harran, had secretly consecrated the hair
of their heads as a promissory "hair offering" to the gods as
the price of their safe arrival. (Ceremonies of "cutting-off" or
mutilations of the face, ears, fingers, or body were common
among early peoples who believed that the gods just could not
resist the appeal of such devotion.) Now Abraham's people
were ready, again, to make a "cutting-off" sacrifice if they could
be sure it would bring the family into closer harmony with
Canaan's unseen powers.

The drought was, however, but the prelude to further
disaster.

The farmers were on the point of harvesting what little
barley there was, when, almost before they knew what was
happening, the dreaded southeast wind was upon them. Its
devastating force swept across the valleys with a violence far
greater than any other such storm Abraham's family had encountered in Canaan. It tore tents from their ground pegs. It
blackened and uprooted vegetation in the fields, laid low the
grain, and withered the grapevines. It bent the branches of

the gnarled old olive trees to its will and uprooted less hardy trees. Its hot blast dried up springs and water holes. Whirlwinds of fine, desert dust made breathing so difficult that the slightest exertion was exhausting to man and beast.

This, then, was the famed "east wind," the *sirocco*, the country's greatest affliction. This was all the gods of Canaan let loose — unpredictable, uncontrollable, unappeasable. This was the fierce, ravaging, incalculable sirocco!

When the storm was over, it was days and days before Abraham's family could re-establish its circle of tents and appraise its deaths and losses. In the weeks that followed, one natural misfortune seemed to follow another in the South Country until it was only a question of time until the shortage of food and fodder would be as devastating as the elements.

"Can you not see by what curse these afflictions cover the land?" the Canaanites asked their soothsayers. "Can you not tell us by what sacrifice they can be taken away?" So many winters without adequate water provision, the dews so scanty, the sirocco so fierce — where was it all to end?

One day Abraham went to the gate of the city to see how other men were solving their famine problem. He found the usual proportion of foreign and native born, for the cities of Canaan were full of foreign settlers; but the men were dull and languid and the gathering by the gate lacked its usual spirit.

The situation was much too grim for jesting, yet a roguish Aramaean, whose impish humor was hard to down, sat on the edge of the assembly and plucked mournfully on his one-stringed instrument, chanting tenderly,

> "O, the gardens of Damascus are fair
> Seven-fold are its streams,
> Of its water there is no end. . . ."

It was a provocative theme, intended to aggravate the other men and thus to relieve the singer's own boredom and help him forget, for the moment, his pangs of hunger. He repeated it over and over, without so much as a sly glance to betray his intent.

Even the apathy of famine has its limits. A big, melancholy

fellow with drooping jowls and hungry eyes turned on him in anger, shouting with exasperation, "Enough! have done with your mirages."

But the jester knew no mercy. "Hast never stood on a bridge in Damascus, that pearl of cities — by moonlight, let us say — and seen the dark water rush swiftly by?" he asked with airy cruelty.

His victim's eyes narrowed. "Scum of the Aramaeans," he answered — and his jaw was set and his lips were dry — "who but you would rebuke with his jests men who have neither tears left to their eyes nor spittle to their tongues, and whose heads are dizzy with thirst? Take your music and be gone!" But others took up the argument, boastfully.

"There is no famine in the Hittite country. Why don't we all go north?" chided one of the group. But no one believed him.

"Such blasphemy! We would but moisten our front teeth in that fellow's country," boasted a Mesopotamian. "It is the irrigation of the Tigris valley you should see. We have *floods* of water!"

"You fail to mention the disaster of those floods when the water breaks through your channels and canals, you of the proud 'black-headed,' " added a third with mock civility. Now the men were enjoying themselves: the assembly by the gate had become its own argumentative self.

"A bee sting is what you need! Only send a bee to waken the weather-god [59] and the Hittite valleys fill with rain!" persisted the Hittite.

"By the beard of my grandfather! Must we listen to this *nig-nag* of a boaster?"

The Aramaean strummed dolefully on.

None of these men had any intention of leaving the country because of Canaan's famine and drought, yet, whenever disaster struck Canaan, each foreigner was ready to extol the superior climatic conditions of his native land. Especially was this true of the Egyptians, whose role in Canaan, however, was more often that of trader or tax-collector than settler in the country.

Now a soft-voiced Canaanite in a herdsman's skirt inter-

rupted, suggesting scornfully, "You city men! You can do no
more than look westward for rain, but we shepherds sniff the
wind and smell sweet water in the ground."

"All shepherds are boasters! He is as thirsty as we!"
shouted the Hittite. Meanwhile the Aramaean brightened his
song in an effort to keep the argument lively.

An Egyptian who had stood, arrogantly, looking down on
the contention, moved over to Abraham's side. So boastful were
the Egyptians at other times, it surprised Abraham that the
tax-collector should draw him aside to speak. The Egyptian,
however, felt that even a cruel jest was better than none if it
served to relieve the monotony that had settled on the gathering at the gate. He saw no reason to interrupt this diversion
which he, too, was enjoying.

"Go to Egypt," he said abruptly to Abraham. "Take your
family and go south to my country. There the fields are green,
the valleys wide, and all good things for man and beast are to
be found in abundance." Casually, he returned to his former
place. A strange fellow, that tax-collector, thought Abraham.

The last strains of the Aramaean's "O, the gardens of
Damascus are fair" were drowned by raucous ribaldry at the
gate, as Abraham turned and walked slowly home. This was
not the first time he had heard the abundance of Egypt ex-
tolled. He recalled how other Egyptians had boasted to him
about their fruitful country.

Again and again in the next few weeks, Abraham pondered
the Egyptian's advice. He watched the grain supply dwindle,
the milk grow pale. He saw his scouts return at nightfall, their
beasts of burden laden with less and less water from ever more
distant wells.

There was no green herbage for the animals to find: even
under the north side of the acacia trees it had disappeared. In
desolation, the senna plant put forth its head of yellow blossoms, but the sheep had to be driven away from it, lest they
eat the noxious weed and die. At the shrinking water-holes
there was contention among the herdsmen as to whose animals
should drink first and how long they should drink.

There was tension, too, among the stay-at-homes: tempers
are brittle when men and women never quite satisfy their needs

of food and water. Even the children learned to share a gourd-ful of water by mouthfuls, when any one of them could have drained it to the last drop. They learned, too, to clack a thumb-nail against their front teeth — the ancestral sign of hunger.

Egypt seemed to be the only answer to Abraham's problem. Perhaps it was the Lord's answer, he thought, as he called his family together and announced, "Let us see for ourselves how great is the bounty of this land."

Again, the camp site buzzed with expectancy. Nor was Abraham himself less curious. What was this land of Egypt? What of its gods? Would he find in Egypt some new manifesta-tion of the great, protecting power he was forever seeking? Did Egypt have great gods like the Sumerians' Inanna and Enlil and Nannar, or lesser gods like Bau and Pa-sag, or family gods such as his *teraphim* represented? Or did her people look to a Lord of all the earth, a Baal, for protection and guidance, like the Canaanites? Would there be, perhaps, a special "lord" in Egypt who would watch over Abraham's caravan? Perhaps Abraham asked his Canaanite neighbors, who at other times had found food in Egypt, these very questions. And perhaps their answers had left him more confused than ever as to what to expect.

Who was this *Re-Atum* to whom the Egyptians were said to credit the creation of the world? And who was *Osiris?* And what was this strange belief that claimed that Egypt's king had not had a human father like other men, but was instead the son of (the) god?

. . . And Abraham went down into Egypt to sojourn there; for the famine was grievous in the land.[60]

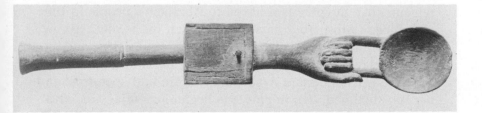

17

Egyptian Interlude

It is not the Biblical legend of Abraham's visit to Egypt that I would picture for you so much as a little corner of Egypt itself and the wonder and surprise with which Abraham and his family must surely have viewed the already ancient customs of the Egypt of his day.

Here was a land teeming with life and prosperity in one of the great eras of a great civilization (Egypt's Twelfth Dynasty). Self-contained though Egypt was, the country was within *walking* distance of Canaan; and there were roads and a line of ancient Canaanite cities that stretched through Canaan's Negeb (South Country) to the very doors of the Pharaoh's summer palace.

What would a famine-wracked people from Canaan have seen there at that time, and how did the land, the people, their life, and their thinking compare and contrast with what Abraham's family had experienced and seen and believed in Mesopotamia and Canaan? And how significant is the fact that, after the visit, we find no trace of Egyptian influence in Abraham's religion, although the gods of Mesopotamia and Canaan affected it deeply? These are the points, and not neccessarily the story in Genesis,[61] that make the Egyptian sojourn important background in our enlarged picture of Abraham.

For however distorted the original story may, or may not, have become through its long years of oral tradition,[62] the fact remains that Egypt was a haven to Abraham's people in time of famine, a prosperous haven from which the family returned "very rich in cattle, in silver, and in gold" and slaves; and one of those slaves, a woman named *Hagar*, became, traditionally, the ancestress of certain Arab tribes. From that ancestress and her son stemmed, too, in part, the beginnings of age-old rivalries still smoldering between Arabs and Jews in the Middle East.

114

Semite women in a caravan travelling between Canaan and Egypt, from a wall painting in the tomb of Knemhotep at Benihasan, Egypt.

The territorial disputes of the borders of Egypt and the lands to the northeast of Egypt are not new in history. They were current in Abraham's day and even before. They developed from contentions arising between the unsettled population and the settled — between "the settled and the sown."

For generations, famine-stricken nomads from the "wilderness" that surrounded the South Country of Canaan, as well as wandering adventurers from even more distant lands, had been creeping into the outskirts of fertile Egypt. They came with envy burning in their hearts.

"By what right do these Egyptians occupy this fruitful land and live upon plenty," the nomads had cried, "while we exist like buzzards in a land of scorpions and drought, and rolls of hunger echo in our hollow maws?" Some of these marauders had made swift, sneak attacks to raid the grain fields and the cattle byres of both Egypt and Canaan; and then they fled. Others crossed the desert to pilfer the rich mining communities, clustered around the copper, turquoise, and gold mines which Egypt's rulers maintained east of the Nile.

For centuries before Abraham, and even to this day, such adventurers, in small bands, have invaded Egypt and Canaan (Palestine), coming back, year after year, to live off the land and pillage the established homes and farms and orchards and industries of their more sedentary neighbors. And one day their raids are successful enough and their envy sufficient, to keep them in the new location. Gradually, they take over the very life that for years they have railed against. Now, *they* are of "the sown," and they fortify themselves against the depredations of other predatory invaders. By such invasions, in ancient days, was Canaan's population, again and again, renewed.

By the time of its Twelfth Dynasty (Abraham's time),[63] Egypt had had enough of these pilfering *'Apiru* (wanderers). Some of them came from the desert; others were Asiatics, Semites, Akkadians — with sprinklings, perhaps, of Hurrians, Hittites, and the first Hyksos — and these, when they came for no good purpose, Egypt was determined to keep out of her territories. So almost the first thing that Abraham's people encountered when they reached the border of Egypt was a massive wall that had just been built (Twelfth Dynasty) at

A Semite and his donkey travelling to Egypt, from a wall painting
in the tomb of Knemhotep at Benihasan, Egypt.

the isthmus which separated Egypt and the desert that led to Canaan. Here, Abraham must persuade the cautious men who were stationed at the wall to keep out any raiding *'Apiru* that he and his people had not come to Egypt as the poor nomads came, intent upon pilfering, but as wealthy herdsmen who needed food and pasturage and had ample means to buy it. Abraham had not come to Egypt because he was poor, but because he had grown too rich for the land of Canaan to support him when the seasonal rains failed to fall. Nor did he intend to stay in Egypt for more than a few seasons, or a few years at best. So the Egyptian border guards welcomed him and his family as they welcomed any well-to-do travelers coming to trade.

To Abraham and his people it must have seemed that everything in Egypt was different. The contrasts were spectacular. The countryside that had been brown and seared by the scorching sun in the Negeb of Canaan, turned, almost overnight, into green fields and flowering swamps in the damper climate of northern Egypt. It was a new experience for them to see fowlers drawing their nets on large numbers of birds in swamps where lotus blossoms, papyrus plants, and palm trees added color to the scene. But the swamps could be foul and fever-ridden in districts where the huts of the fishmongers' villages crowded too closely together on the steamy shores of the delta.

Sometimes, as they traveled westward, a damp Mediterranean breeze made the nights so cold that the woolen garments that Abraham and his people had worn in Canaan to keep out the burning heat of the South Country were needed to provide warmth and comfort overnight in Egypt. Yet Egypt was a warm country.

How different the people looked and dressed in Egypt! A simple white kilt that reached from hips to knees seemed to be the costume of both princes and commoners. Curious but not unfriendly Egyptians gaped at these foreigners in their strange, long, full costumes. Naked children playing carefree in the sun stopped their games to watch them, while hungry

An Egyptian (time of Abraham).

Egyptian dogs, searching for any morsel of discarded food, scurried about, barking.

The abundance of fruit and vegetables and fish in the markets of Egypt's cities and the many fields of waving barley and wheat along the countryside must have been welcome sights to Abraham's family. Often, across the fields, they heard the songs of the Egyptian reapers and, from a greater distance, came herding songs and the plaintive tones of the shepherds' lament.

As soon as arrangements could be made, Abraham would have purchased the right to settle his family, probably on the outskirts of one of the delta cities, where his flocks and herds could graze and where his people could plant seeds and gather their own harvests.

Everything in Egypt continued to be of interest to the newcomers. In the bakers' and brewers' shops the women grinding the grain, the bakers molding their loaves, the brewers stamping with their bare feet upon their mash of bread-crumbs, yeast, and water, or straining and bottling their brew — all these reminded Abraham of his boyhood in Ur where, as in Canaan also, bread and beer were staples for both men and gods.

The weavers' shops and the butcher shops and the granaries and embalmers' shops and the little booths in the market place were different from anything he had seen in Canaan. Also new to his experience were the Egyptian scribes who seemed always to be standing or sitting about with stylus and papyrus "paper" in their hands, ready to record some sale. And those picturesque hieroglyphics they drew, how unlike the simple cuneiform markings which boys like Abraham had learned to make on clay tablets in the schools in Ur! Even the harvests required a steward and a scribe: the one to pass out the sickles and bindings to the slaves, the other to record every sheaf of golden grain that went into the storage barns.

There were daily processions of women to be seen carrying food — baked meats in covered clay containers, live ducks, bread, baskets of fruit, and jars of beer; but how could Abraham's people know that these were offerings being taken to the priests who maintained the endowed tombs of dead noblemen?

Procession of offering-bearers: a wooden model (time of Abraham).

It had been many years since, as a boy, Abraham had watched ship-builders on the Euphrates shore putting their small boats together and sealing them with pitch. What now did Abraham think as he saw ship-builders on the Nile making a thirty-foot sail boat, not for fishermen to use in their daily fishing trips, but to be placed in a tomb to carry some noble-man's soul down the great River of Death to the underworld? The Mesopotamians had never been sure of immortality; the Egyptians took it for granted!

Early in his visit, Abraham must have sensed the Egyp-tians' concern about life after death. So many of their craftsmen were as busy making household furnishings and jewelry and ornaments to be buried in tombs for use of the dead in the after-world as they were making the same objects for the use of the living! For generations, such faithful toilers had expected nothing for themselves after death yet had never seemed to doubt that their kings and noblemen would live forever; but now the priests of Egypt were promising even commoners and slaves that they would all "live like kings" beyond the grave.[64]

Whether, outside some carpenter's shop men were building a mortuary boat for some nobleman's tomb or in a tiny work-room they were fashioning delicate jewelry for a royal princess, the workmen seemed happy. Even the slaves, whose work was both laborious and monotonous, expected little more in life than the companionship their tasks supplied: they knew no other pattern of living than to obey and be taken care of by their superiors. Their faces were bland and their motions rhythmic as they cut the grain or beat the gold or raised the sail, or even harpooned a crocodile. No longer were Egypt's slaves required to spend their lives in creating the massive pyramids of an earlier age: her kings were content now with more modest mausoleums and the slaves worked on such various projects of domestic architecture and engineering as temples and defense walls and irrigation improvements.

A deep sense of social justice had developed in this unique dynasty. "I gave to the beggar; I nourished the orphan"; "do right" and "deal justly with all" — these were but a few of the popular admonitions and claims of official administrators at the time. Corruption was by no means nonexistent, but at least

Limestone stela (time of Abraham).

Granite stela, showing Egyptian hieroglyphics and symbolic sun-disc and hawk's wings of the sun-gods Re-Atum and Horus.

the ideal of truth and fair treatment was fashionable, and an expectation of justice pervaded all classes. Even Abraham could sense that in his day Egypt was a good country and a prosperous haven.

Perhaps what immediately surprised Abraham's people were not so much the simple scenes of daily life in Egypt as the temples and statues and stelae that they encountered in the cities and along the highways. Yet only a few of these antiquities can be seen today because most of the cities of the delta as Abraham's generation knew them now lie beneath the waters of the Mediterranean Sea.

Egypt's temples bore little resemblance to those of Canaan. The people's houses were made of perishable clay and brick and straw, but the temples for the gods were built of stone to last "forever." They were simple in design, but often stately with high and massive pillars. On the temples' walls, brightly colored paintings pictured the exploits of gods and kings and were easier for ignorant Egyptians and foreigners to read than the hieroglyphics beside the pictures.

Limestone and granite were used, not only for the temples, but for obelisks and stelae and mammoth statues unlike anything to be seen in Canaan or Mesopotamia. The statues represented gods and kings and were set high on massive pedestals. They were inscribed in a language Abraham's family could not read, but the faces of the granite kings were kind, as if Egypt's sun had warmed their stony hearts.

The top of each slender obelisk tapered gently to a four-sided point, known as the *pyramidion,* and it shone out brightly, perpetuating the name and fame, not of the god alone, but of the king who had erected the obelisk. Smaller stelae recorded national and individual successes, and noblemen as well as kings provided temples in honor of various gods.

There were hundreds of gods to be honored. In Egypt, almost every mysterious power and attribute of nature and the animal world was personified by a god; and every deeply felt need of the heart was fulfilled in the thought of a protector or guide. We can but wonder how Abraham felt about the many images and paintings of these gods which he saw in temples

Granite column, "papyrus" pattern, reminiscent of pre-dynastic
bunches-of-reeds posts (time of Abraham).

Egyptian image: wooden Shawabti figure (time of Abraham). Such images were commonly placed in Egyptian tombs to relieve the deceased of any labor in the realm of the dead.

and homes and on the highways. What did he think of the animal heads and faces given to so many of them — the hawk head for *Re-Atum* and *Horus*, the cow head for *Hathor*, the lioness head for *Seknet*, or the ibis head for *Thoth?* He could scarcely have understood the meanings and the history of these

Limestone relief from a funerary temple (XII Dynasty).

combinations of animal and human forms. Did Abraham sense the mysterious powers the Egyptians felt were manifest in such forms? Or was he repulsed by the images, as tradition pictures he had been repulsed when, long before, as a young man, he had angrily broken the sacred images his father had kept for sale in his shop in Ur?

Stranger to Abraham than the obelisks, the temples, and even the animal-headed gods, however, was the climate and the fact that, in the Egyptians' cloudless country, *it never rained,* yet vegetables and fruits grew in abundance and enormous harvests of barley and wheat were gathered year after year. Abraham had left Canaan because of the lack of seasonal rain; he had come to a country where rain was virtually unknown, and yet the land was fertile! In Canaan, the Lord Baal hurled his thunderbolts and the rain fell from the sky. In Egypt, people said, Osiris, god of the Nile River, brought water to the land from beneath the earth, from a subterranean source in the world of the dead. Each New Year, the river rose and overflowed its banks and Osiris flooded the fields with life-giving water. No wonder the Egyptians worshiped the river — so powerful, so dependable that they could even forecast the day of its uprising. No wonder they thought that the land of the dead, Osiris' land, could be beautiful and enjoyable and everlasting, knowing that this great blessing came to them from the underworld.

But Osiris was only one of the three great forces that dominated Egyptian life — *the river, the sun,* and *the king.* Each day, a bold and brassy sun rose and cut the cloudless Egyptian sky, east to west, with spectacular exactness. Each evening it sailed over the western horizon and disappeared, Egyptians said, into Osiris' realm of the dead. Through mysterious, subterranean streams, not unlike those traveled by the dead, it crossed Osiris' underworld, returned to life, and rose again reborn next morning to gladden the day for men and beasts. *Re,* sometimes called *Re-Atum* to signify his all-inclusive creative powers, was the Egyptians' sun-god; and *Horus* was his son. Only the hawks seen flying high in the sky dared to approach the sun. So the hawks' wing became the sun-gods'

Limestone relief from a funerary temple (XI Dynasty), showing familiar symbols of Re-Atum and Horus: the sun-disc and hawk's wings of divinity and the uraeus of kingship.

symbol, and Re's people desired nothing else quite so much as to live "under the shadow of his wings."

In Egypt, so long as the sun rose, reborn, each morning and the Nile's annual inundation flooded the fields, the fertility of the land could be taken for granted. Not so in Canaan. Fertility — which is still a problem in that country — was the major concern of the Canaanites. They just had to have abundant harvests, many flocks and herds, and large families to defend, feed, and perpetuate themselves. The festivals that grew out of Canaan's earliest rituals and religious plays were based upon her people's need to reawaken vegetation after the long, dark, winter days in a country that had no Nile to flood its fields and no Euphrates to fill irrigation canals. Yet, Egypt too celebrated her New Year.

Perhaps Abraham and his family remembered similar ceremonies in Harran when they attended Egypt's New Year's Eve festivities and watched the giant bonfires along the Nile that, at midnight on the eve of the solstice, signalized the returning light and warmth of Nature. Perhaps they saw one of the many processions of priests wending their way to the river's edge, each carrying high above it in a sacred shrine a small image of the Babe Osiris, which, for the occasion, had been taken from its place in one of the various temples. After the story of the birth of the god had been recited to the crowd that gathered on the riverbank, the figure of the infant god was dipped into the water and lifted out again, to symbolize the birth of the river god. Then, the priests held the sacred image high above the crowd and the people shouted, "The heavenly virgin has brought forth! The light of the world is waxing strong!" Finally, in a burst of joy, musicians played their harps and flutes while the people danced and sang.

It was sometimes difficult for Abraham to explain to his people what he learned about Egypt's gods. Even if he told his family that the Egyptians' Re, Horus, and Hathor could be equated, in some ways, with the Mesopotamian An, Enlil, and Inanna, and that in certain respects the death of Osiris was like that of the dying-rising gods of the Mesopotamians and Canaanites, there was still the divinity of the king to be accounted for. For however powerful the sun- and the river-gods

Limestone relief from a funerary temple (XII Dynasty).

appeared to the Egyptians, equally compelling was the prestige of the third great force that dominated Egyptian life. That was Egypt's king, called — in later years — the *pharaoh*.

In Mesopotamia, each New Year the Mesopotamian was harassed and apprehensive lest he, or his city's king, lose the gods' favor in the allotments the gods were passing out for the year ahead. He made frantic propitiations to the unseen forces. He watched the stars eagerly for changes which he called divine directives, never feeling secure in this world and never expecting life in a world to come, since man had yet to discover the fruit of immortality. Nor was the Canaanite more secure in his mind than the Mesopotamian: Canaan's princes, too, were mortal and vulnerable, and Canaan's gods, also, were capricious.[65]

With the Egyptian it was otherwise. His king was a god, he said, the incarnation on earth of both Re and Osiris; in fact, the pharaoh represented all the gods in his regal capacity. The god Re had been the first, the *ideal*, king of their country, they said, and all subsequent kings were born of him. (Even a commoner, who, with a band of malcontents, might seize the power and establish a new dynasty, became, overnight, a *son of Re* — not figuratively, for the people believed the fiction — with no question of inconsistency.) All Egypt's kings were then "the sons of [the] god." One had only to serve the king, the god, by obeying the officials who represented him, and both this life and the world to come were assured. Still, after death, each man's deeds must be weighed in the balance, good and evil, against a feather which was *Truth*. So, except where a cruel king or overseer exploited the slaves, Egyptians at this time were a joyous, confident people, living in a country that demanded very little labor to produce what food, clothes, shelter and pleasures they required.

For all the success and prosperity of the times — and this was one of Egypt's most prosperous dynasties — and for all the beauty of its art and skill of its craftsmen, simplicity was still the keynote of Egyptian life. The king wore the simple kilt of his people and the same type of unpretentious headdress that had satisfied his ancestors for generations; and he and his family walked barefooted as often as not. The same simplicity was

An Egyptian king: a wooden statuette (XII Dynasty, time of Abraham).

evident in their living: the king, looking quite human in spite of his "divinity," was often seen out walking with his vizier and noblemen. But although, during this period of history, Egypt's kings mingled more naturally and freely with the people than in the more majestic days of later dynasties, still the pharaoh was a god to his subjects and they gave him reverence and unquestioning obedience.

They traveled often to the sacred shrines where the king and his nobles paid homage to the gods. At the seasonal festivals, all work was set aside and the population gathered to watch the colorful processions, led by the priests, and the king perhaps, that wound their way through the streets, or into the fields, or along the river bank to the site chosen for the ceremonies.

Just what festivals Abraham and his people were able to attend in Egypt we can hardly say. Living in the delta, as they did, the family would have had to travel many miles to some of the most sacred sites; but such pilgrimages, near and far, were perennial to the Egyptians. Perhaps they visited the sun temple at Heliopolis which claimed to have been the site of the "primeval hillock" from which the (Egyptians') "world" was supposed to have been created. Perhaps they traveled still farther south, to Abydos, and saw the new temple (Twelfth Dynasty) and, with it, the great walled area where favored noblemen were promised burial within the sacred site. Here, the ancient Egyptian pageants were dramatized most elaborately. Here, in the drama of Creation, they would have seen the creator-god, *Atum* — from whom Re-Atum took his name — overcome chaos and darkness as, "for the first time," the sun rose "out of the deep."

Here, too, the drama of the birth, death, and resurrection of Osiris (symbolizing the annual life and death of vegetation) was enacted every year. The Osiris drama began with a series of acts which included, among others, a bloody mock battle between the two brothers, Osiris and Seth — symbolizing good and evil. Osiris was slain and his body thrown into the river, and the dark days of winter followed his passing. The drama ended when, triumphantly, their sister Isis brought back the body of Osiris from the dark underworld and restored it to life on earth (spring). Then followed, in triumph, the Egyptians' greatest processional, the "Great Annual Procession of Osiris!"

Such superb and dramatic festivals could scarcely have failed to interest Abraham's people. Perhaps his family contrasted them with simpler ceremonies they had seen in Harran and Canaan and recognized the common need of all peoples to express their thankfulness for life and light and vegetation and to appeal hopefully to powers beyond their control and understanding.

Unfortunately the ancient traditions regarding Abraham give us little about his experiences in Egypt except to explain Abraham's wealth and to offer a brief narrative to indicate Sarah's charm and the misfortune it caused.

When they had entered Egypt, the legend explains, Abraham had pleaded with Sarah, saying, "You are a fair woman to look upon. If it is said, 'She is his wife,' the Egyptians will kill me and save you, and I shall die because of you. Say you are my sister in order that I shall live." And Sarah had agreed.

Although the pharaoh's capital was farther south, in the vicinity of Memphis, we know that each summer Egypt's kings came north to enjoy the cool Mediterranean breezes. It may have been while vacationing in his summer palace in the delta that the king first met Abraham, Sarah, and Lot. These foreigners, coming as they did from the cities of Mesopotamia and Canaan, were "world travelers" to the Egyptian nobles, some of whom, having been on expeditions to Canaan, understood the Semitic language. Perhaps some of the noblemen had invited Abraham and Lot to games and sports and had made possible some excursions for Abraham's family. There had been gifts from the nobles who wished to ingratiate themselves with these foreign visitors: braces of ducks, a high-prowed marsh skiff, a gaming board; for Abraham a slave or two perhaps; and for Lot a bow or a fowler's net for fishing and hunting trips.

There were presents from the pharaoh too: for the women, furnishings for their household, jewelry (for which Egypt was at that time famous), fruits, or a silver bowl perhaps; and for the men, fat-tailed sheep and Egyptian oxen and other superior cattle from the royal byres.

An Egyptian woman (time of Abraham).

The difference between Sarah's status, as the wife of a chieftain from Harran and Canaan, and the status of the less-traveled wives of the king and the noblemen's wives was evident in the assurance and grace with which Sarah carried herself. This grace, no less than the Aramaean features of her face, gave Sarah a beauty unlike that of Egyptian women and attracted the king's attention.

"Was she beautiful?" men in later centuries used to ask, referring to Sarah, the wife of their beloved hero.

"So beautiful that even the mighty Pharaoh of Egypt remarked upon it!" was the answer. What greater proof could they demand? And so the tradition of Sarah's beauty grew and persisted and was recorded in Genesis in the Old Testament; in the *Book of Jubilees* or *Little Genesis;* and in at least one of the newly discovered so-called Dead Sea Scrolls which says in part: "And how beautiful the look of her face . . . And how fine is the hair of her head, how fair indeed are her eyes and how pleasing her nose and all the radiance of her face. . . . And above all women she is lovely and higher is her beauty than that of them all, and with all her beauty there is much wisdom in her. . . ."[66]

(These scrolls, discovered by chance in an obscure cave, in 1947, by an Arab boy exploring a forbidding ravine near the northwestern shore of the Dead Sea, presumably had been hidden in the cave just before the Destruction of Jerusalem (70 A.D.) by men who never lived to come back for them. The manuscripts — only one of which is identified with Genesis — were written, some on thin sheets of leather and some on copper which had badly oxidized. They had been rolled in linen and stored in tall, cylindrical jars. They were unrolled and transcribed with great difficulty and patient effort, and appear to have been written some time not earlier than 150 B.C.E.)

Sarah pleased and amused the Pharaoh, and he invited her to the palace. Her tongue could be witty as well as sharp, perhaps; and it was not many months before she was enjoying a not unwelcome popularity in the royal household.

At about this time, by coincidence, a "plague" arose and

Semites in Egypt, from a wall painting of Ibsha (right) and his
caravan of Asiatics in the tomb of Knemhotep at Benihasan, Egypt
(time of Abraham).

threatened Egypt. Like all his people, the king believed that such afflictions were punishments inflicted by an angry god. One by one, the Egyptian gods were propitiated, but to no effect. Then the king became suspicious of Sarah's god and inquired more fully into her background.

The pharaohs of Egypt were surrounded by carping noblemen and ambitious administrators, competing in devious ways for the favor of their "god"-king. Yet the god, the king, was human enough to be capricious. He was sated by the adulation of both men and women in his court, to whom his slightest wish was a divine injunction. That Abraham, whom he had befriended and feted and rewarded, should have tricked him was unthinkable to the king. Therefore, when he learned that Sarah was Abraham's wife, the royal anger blazed and he sent Sarah back to Abraham with the command that Abraham and all his tribe leave the country.

And Abram went up out of Egypt, he, and his wife, and all that he had, and Lot with him, into the south. And Abram was very rich in cattle, in silver, and in gold.

Thus Abraham returned to Canaan, his religious convictions unchanged by his Egyptian sojourn.

18

Lot's Choice

The country that aproned the Amorite mountain was more inviting to Abraham than the South Country of Canaan. The plain of Mamre, the heights of Uru-salem, Luz, and Ai where he had built the altar, all lay northward over rising mountain roads. They were beautiful to remember: the first overlooked the valleys that stretched to the Great Sea, the second crowned the slopes that fell away eastward to the Salt Sea, and the third, the most spectacular of all, took all Canaan to its heart. It was the mountains of Canaan that were urging Abraham northward. First in memory and then in fact, their outlines came back to him.

We see the bulky caravan, swollen by the Pharaoh's gifts of sheep and oxen and other livestock and by the additional pack animals that were needed to transport the personal treasures Abraham's family had accumulated in Egypt. We hear the rhythm of sharp little hooves clattering over the loose fragments of limestone and shale that litter the mountain roads of Canaan's Negeb. We sense Abraham's longing for his mountain home, "the place where his tent had been in the beginning, between Beth-el and Ai," and for "the altar which he had made there at the first." With him, we count the days and measure the miles: the pace of the journey is set by the needs of his browsing sheep.

During the years in Egypt, Abraham had gathered additional servants and slaves into his "family," and Sarah had acquired, among others, *Hagar*, a young woman from a South Country tribe who had been a slave in Egypt when Sarah found her. Now Lot, as well as Abraham and Sarah, "had flocks and herds and tents." Not only his livestock and servants but the number of young men who were Lot's particular followers, and their families, had increased with the years: they were enough now to make a "family" quite apart from Abraham.

141

There was rivalry during the journey, and bitter disputes arose between Lot's herdsmen and Abraham's. For water-holes and pastures — or merely for the excitement of the contests — the men wrangled and fought. Yet Lot and Abraham were "kinsmen," a word not to be taken lightly.

Abraham returned to the land he had learned to love, happy to be at home again in Canaan's mountains, but disturbed that the peace the mountains always suggested to him was lacking in his household. Even on the fertile slopes that surrounded Luz, there was still not pasturage enough for so many additional animals. And the rivalries continued.

Bringing up Lot, his brother's son, was the nearest Abraham had come to parenthood; the boy had been dear to him and Sarah. But Lot was a man now, and a man must live a life of his own choosing and follow a god of his own choice. As Terah had sacrificed to *his* gods and Abraham, choosing, had left those gods behind, so, Abraham realized, Lot must be made free to bring up his family as he would.

Abraham called Lot to him and said to his brother's son,

Let there be no strife, I pray thee, between me and thee, and between my herdsmen and thy herdsmen; for we be brethren.

Is not the whole land before thee? separate thyself, I pray thee, from me: if thou wilt take the left hand, then I will go to the right; or if thou depart to the right hand, then I will go to the left. And Lot lifted up his eyes, and beheld all the plain of Jordan, that it was well watered everywhere . . . like the land of Egypt. . . .[67]

Lot looked eastward over the wide expanse. He thought of the verdant plain of Jordan, the plain that men then called "the garden of the Lord" because of its fertility. He remembered, too, the cities of the plain and their princes, some of whom he already knew.

The cities of Canaan's lowlands had much in common with Mesopotamia's cities. They were old and sophisticated. The level of their cultural achievement, at that time, was unbelievably high; in art and music especially they seem to have excelled their neighbors to the north and east. Their markets were brisk. And the pace of their city life was lively.

Lot was young. Lot was rich. Like Abraham, he had prospered in Egypt. He could well afford the diversions and luxuries the cities provided. Indeed, the quiet, contemplative days of a semi-nomad may not have appealed to him as they did to Abraham. He may have missed the urban life he had known in Ur and Harran. He may have been glad to break away, once Abraham had offered him a chance to separate.

And Lot chose all the plain of Jordan and left the mountains of Canaan to Abraham. Henceforth, while his flocks pastured on the slopes above the cities, Lot and his followers, independent of Abraham, would identify themselves and their activities with the people of "the cities of the plain."

Sodom, Gomorrah, Admah, Zeboiim, and *Zoar* — at least we know by name these "cities of the plain"; each governed by its prince, its "king"; confederates in case of attack. Confederates in worship, too, perhaps, since archaeologists have found, on a hillside overlooking the Salt Sea, the ruins of a spacious, elaborate site that must have accommodated hundreds of pilgrims from these cities at that time and witnessed many ancient festivals of worship.[68]

When the choice was made, the contentions were forgotten. Now Abraham and Lot were kinsmen, parting. It was a time for ceremonials, for an exchange of gifts, for lavish sacrifice of oxen and sheep. A goat must be sent forth alone into the wilderness to be the "scapegoat" that would carry away and wipe out, by its symbolic destruction, all the misdeeds and mistakes and contentions of the family. There must be festivals of parting and songs of *God-speed* in which their Canaanite neighbors, too, might join.

It was a time for celebration. Their finest Egyptian linens and their most colorful robes were none too elaborate for the occasion. It demanded their most elegant jewelry — necklaces and more necklaces, bracelets, anklets; nose rings, ear rings, finger rings. It called for feasting and dancing and wine. It demanded songs and prayers and "charms."

When the time for actual parting came, many of Abraham's people accompanied Lot's family for a mile or two. Others stayed behind to straighten up the camp site. The celebration was over. The shepherds returned to their sheep, the herdsmen to their cattle. And Abraham returned to the quiet altar, still strewn with evidence of the festival.

Abraham and his brother's son had separated after many years of companionship. Lot had chosen the rich plain of Jordan and journeyed east where he would pitch his tents toward Sodom, while Abraham remained in the hill country.

But the men of Sodom were wicked and sinners before the Lord exceedingly.[69]

How peaceful the land of Canaan must have seemed to Abraham as, from the heights at Luz, he surveyed the portion left to him! Bounded on the east by the ridge that sloped to the Jordan river-bed and on the west by the blue waters of the Mediterranean (the Great Sea), in waves of peaks and plains the land stretched north and south as far as eyes could see.

Standing beside the altar his people had built, Abraham was a man full of faith in his own destiny. Surely, he reasoned, the Lord god would not forever leave him childless.

And the Lord said unto Abram, after that Lot was separated from him, Lift up thine eyes, and look from the place where thou art northward, and southward, and eastward, and westward. For all the land which thou seest, to thee will I give it, and to thy seed forever. And I will make thy seed as the dust of the earth: so that if a man can number the dust of the earth, then shall thy seed also be numbered.

Arise, walk through the land in the length of it and in the breadth of it: for I will give it unto thee.[70]

It was not hard for Abraham to believe that, in this holy spot, the Lord on High was speaking and directing him.

There was a plain a little to the south where the prince of Mamre already had made Abraham welcome to settle. It, too, was on the Amorite Mountain; fertile and well-watered. And the prince of Mamre was his friend.

Then Abram removed his tent, and came and dwelt in the plain of Mamre, . . . and built there an altar unto the Lord.[71]

19

The Battle of the Kings

Up and down among the cities of western Canaan went Egypt's tax collectors, since, nominally at least, Canaan was Egyptian-controlled in Abraham's time. But the hand of Egypt was light as long as Canaan's princes paid their tribute and Canaan's ports continued to act as forwarding points between Egypt and the countries to the east. However, Egyptians were not the only tax collectors in Canaan.

To the east, across the Jordan River gorge, a line of Canaanite settlements followed the trade route that led from Damascus to copper mines south of the Salt (Dead) Sea. Conquerors and foreign traders from as far east as Elam on the far side of the Tigris River, on their way to and from the mining district, raided these and other Canaanite settlements periodically. They spared the populations only in exchange for tribute to be paid annually to their officials and the promise of food, water, and peaceful camp sites for their every caravan.

From his friend, the prince of Sodom, Lot soon learned how heavy was the burden of this annual taxation from which the people of the plains gained nothing in return. For twelve years the cities of Sodom, Gomorrah, Admah, Zeboiim, and Zoar had been paying tribute to *Chedorlaomer*, king of Elam; and they were weary of their bargain. By secret agreement, the five princes resolved to defy the foreign tax collector the next time he appeared.

It did not take long for word of his arrival to spread from one city to another. Each prince was waiting for the Elamite delegation when it arrived at his city's gate. Welcoming greetings dripped from their lips like honey overflowing a comb: yes, the Elamites could sleep in the assembly place; yes, their hosts would feed them; yes, they would provide fodder and water for the foreigners' animals. But not so much as a shoestring of goods would Canaan's princes bring forth to load upon

145

the waiting asses! Grain? No. Fabrics? No. Weapons and tools? No, no, no! Furthermore — come to think of it! — why any longer should they provide food every year for these intruders?

The Elamites were at a loss to know what to do. They were in no position, militarily, to enforce their demands in the face of conspiracy. They could only fall back on warnings as to what would happen to the backsliders once the news of their defection reached Elam's king.

Consistently, in each of the five cities the princes' refusals were firm. The agreement to pay tribute had been honored over too many years already, was the popular cry. Alliance of their five cities had made the Canaanites bold. And Elam was far away.

Thus, in the thirteenth year of Elam's domination, her tax collectors went home empty-handed from the vale of Siddim.

Naturally the king of Elam was not pleased. He swore by his beard and all the gods of Elam that the princes' high-handedness would be punished. He would make an example of these westerners, he said, lest more cities along the route to the mineral fields repeat such defiance and cut off his passage to the copper supply. Chedorlaomer needed these cities not only for the booty they provided but, especially, for the food supplies he could appropriate in passing. No alliance of petty princes was going to be allowed to say *No* to him, Chedorlaomer, king of Elam! He had allies of his own. Canaan would be taught a lesson if it took every mercenary from the Tigris to the Nile to put down its insolence. The copper mines would still be within his reach and Canaan would be made to honor him at every water-hole along the route!

Thus, in the fourteenth year came Chedorlaomer himself and his three allies, determined, once and for all, to subdue the Canaanites.[72]

They swaggered down the east side of the Jordan cleft, the unexpectedness of their attacks making up for their lack of mobility. Before any of the cities of Transjordan could call for allies or assemble their "mighty men," the Elamites were upon them.

They smote the "giants" of *Ammon*, the *Zamzummin* by

the *Jabbok* brook, the "terrible men" of *Emin* in the vale of *Kiriathiam*, the *Horites* at *Mt. Seir*. They raided the *Amorites* and destroyed the harvests of the *Amalekites*. Then, flushed with success, they turned to find the five princes of Sodom, Gomorrah, Admah, Zeboiim, and Zoar line up against them in the *vale of Siddim!*

The might of Chedorlaomer, king of Elam, with his three allies — Amraphel, king of Shinar; Arioch, king of Ellasar; and Tidal, "king of the nations" (meaning leader of the foreign recruits and polyglot mercenaries) — was pitted against the power of the five Canaanite princes, four kings against five. And the foreign kings won! Herdsmen, farmers, merchants, and servants augmented the defense, but all of the Canaanite armies went down to defeat in the slime pits of Siddim. Many of the men were slain or taken captive, while others fled to the mountain beseeching the gods of the holy place at *Bab ed Dra* to intervene in their behalf.

Then the eastern conquerors took all the goods they found in Sodom and Gomorrah, the people's weapons and tools, and the people themselves. They feasted upon the Canaanites' supplies and appropriated what remained of the foodstuffs, and went their way northward with their prisoners. And among the prisoners were Lot and the women and servants of his household; and they took his goods as well.

None of the Canaanite cities in the path of the kings' return could be expected to deny food or offer resistance, since Chedorlaomer had been wise enough already to have overcome them on his way south. The King's Highway — as the road has been known ever since that day — was clear; unmolested, he could live off the countryside. In safety he could draw upon the wells and water-holes along the way. If the rate of the king's progress was slow, it was comforting to remember that the length of his caravan and the weight of its burdens was but a measure of the success he had had in teaching the Canaanites a lesson. But Chedorlaomer and his allies had reckoned their triumph without thought of what could be happening on the plain of Mamre.

Among the men who had escaped from the battle in the slime pits of Siddim was one who knew that Abraham, Lot's

kinsman, was living on the plain of the prince of Mamre. To
Abraham he hastened with the bitter news that "the cities of
the plain" in the vale of Siddim had fallen to the eastern kings
and that Lot and his family were being taken north by their
captors.

The blood of Canaan's princes was hot. To pit themselves
against an invader, and more especially to outwit a conqueror,
was to them as much an exciting, welcome diversion as it was
an exercise of justice.

Willingly, eagerly, indignantly, Abraham's neighbors —
his brothers-in-arms — the prince of Mamre, the prince of
Eschol, and the prince of *Aner,* joined his cause. Such provoca-
tion to retaliate had not come to the plains of Mamre for many
a day! Hastily, weapons were collected, supplies made ready,
and servants armed, while the princes conferred as to the best
way to cut off the retreat of the four unsuspecting kings.

Songs of battle ended the ceremonies which started Abraham and his allies in pursuit of the eastern kings. How many
followers the princes Aner, Eschol, and Mamre supplied one
cannot say, but tradition has reported that from Abraham's
own household "318 trained servants, born in his house" were
armed for war. Let the eastern invaders beware: Lot's capture
was not to go unavenged.

In the north, at a settlement called Dan, the two forces
met. There, the cunning of Abraham's night attack caught the
enemy off guard. Some of them fell where they were, others fled
in disorder, leaving their treasures in their wake. Abraham
pressed his advantage, pursuing the easterners all the way to
Hobah, on the route to Damascus. There was no need to go
further. The conquering kings were dead.

Then Abraham and his allies and the people they had
liberated returned, bearing the stolen booty and bringing with
them Lot and his belongings and the women and servants who
had been captured. Long before they could reach Sodom, however, near Uru-salem in the valley of *Shaveh,* they were met
by the grateful king of Sodom and some of his people who had
survived the battle at Siddim. How the hills must have rung
with their shouts of glad recognition!

Quite a company they made as, together, they climbed to

the nearby "high place" of Uru-salem (city of peace), a shrine of the *Jebusites,* where, with Melchizedek, the prince and priest of Salem, they offered a sacrifice of thanksgiving. And what a thanksgiving! Songs of victory and peace proclaimed the people's gratitude to their Lord Most High, and everywhere there was praise for the deliverers.

Abraham divided the spoils, giving a share of the goods to Salem's priest for the Lord of Uru-salem. And the priest said,

"Blessed be Abraham, and blessed be the Most High God which hath delivered thine enemies into thy hand."

The return of his captured people was all the grateful prince of Sodom wished to claim.

"Give me the persons," he said, "and take the goods to yourself."

But Abraham would have none of it.

"Here, I lift up my hand," he said, "and swear by the Lord, the most High God, that I will not take so much as a thread or a shoelacing of anything that is yours, lest you should say, 'By this encounter I have made Abraham rich.' We shall take only so much as our young men have already eaten and the share that belongs to my brothers-in-arms who went with me, Aner, Eschol, and Mamre. Let them take their portion."

The Battle of the Kings was over; it was time for the men to return, each to his own home. There, the fallen kinsmen were not forgotten. The wounded were cared for, the bereaved comforted. In each city, the meaty odors of sacrifice again filled the air as its people sang and danced in another ritual of thanksgiving.

"And the gods loved the sweet savor of the sacrifice!" the people said.

20

A Son for Abraham

The burden of their childlessness was not Sarah's alone. Abraham felt it deeply. In his time and country, to die without sons was a dishonor. A son to bury his father and descendants to perpetuate his name was what they both craved, with the ancient, familiar cry, *Let us make us a name.*

At Harran, Abraham had prayed that, through his descendants, the Lord Most High would make of him a great nation and that all the families of the earth would be blessed by the good works of his children. At Shechem, Abraham had appealed to Canaan's Lord of the earth for assurance that to his descendants this bounteous country might become a homeland.

Abraham's family had now wandered in Canaan for ten years. The number of Abraham's sheep and goats and asses had multiplied many times. The cattle he had brought from Egypt had increased. The many children born to the servants and slaves of his household were growing up into a sizeable group of fine young helpers and potential artisans, shepherds, and herdsmen. Still Abraham and Sarah had no children, and still Eliezer, the steward, was Abraham's legal heir. This man was not even an Aramaean: he had been born in Abraham's household, the son of a native of Damascus.

It pained Abraham deeply to think that he had not even one son to inherit his name and wealth, to bury him and keep his grave in remembrance, and to treasure the family records. The lack of sons was a knife that every day turned in his heart.

He watched the children of his slaves and servants romping and playing their childish games in imitation of the activities of their elders. He saw them throw the javelin and draw taut the bowstring as they fought and hunted in their play; saw them corral the lambs and kids in a noisy imitation of the shepherds; found them bending industriously over straw baskets they were fashioning, and clay pots, and stone axes.

He saw them make pack animals of their fellows and start on mythical journeys. He watched them improvise small tents from scraps of bright colored cloth and saw one little lad strut pompously by, inspecting the scene, and heard him say, "Now I am my lord Abraham and you are my kinsmen!" Was he never to have sons like these?

Often, as he sat under a giant oak tree at Mamre, pondering the situation, Abraham "talked" to the Lord god and was comforted. Especially in the evening, when the west wind stirred the foliage of the mighty tree, Abraham thought he heard the Lord's replies in the rustle of the leaves.

"Lord god," Abraham pleaded, "what wilt thou give me, seeing I go childless and the steward of my house is this Eliezer of Damascus? To me you have given no descendant: and lo, one born in my house is mine heir." The word of the Lord seemed to come back to him, saying the very words he was thinking: "This shall not be thine heir; but he that shall be born of your own flesh and blood shall be thine heir."

This invisible Lord at the oak of Mamre in Canaan, by what form of sacrifice could he be propitiated? Abraham asked himself, craving to believe what he so much wanted to hear, yet scarcely daring to expect the answer. But this Lord god in Canaan to whom Abraham turned so often was the same god who had led him all his days.

"A son, O Lord, a son!" Abraham's prayer was choked with emotion. By what bond could he assure himself that he and the Lord god shared a common desire? He said, daringly, "Lord God, whereby shall I know that I shall inherit it?"[73] Already he had waited ten years in Canaan.

Abraham's friend, the prince of Mamre, was the priest of Mamre. He, too, came to the giant tree for meditation. He came to offer sacrifices upon the nearby altar. He came to interpret the Lord's will to his trusting people. He sympathized with Abraham in his problems and desires. He instructed him in the rituals of his people and repeated what he believed to be the Lord's answer when he said: "Bring me a heifer of three years old, and a she-goat of three years old, and a ram of three years old, and a turtledove and a young pigeon."

Explicitly, Abraham followed the ritual's demands. The

heifer, the goat, the ram, the turtledove and the pigeon were brought to the sanctuary. The priest divided the animals, each into two parts, and laid each piece against the other.

The ceremony that was to follow stemmed from extreme antiquity. It was a ritual of alliance, a pledge of a union of interests. It conveyed the idea that that which had been in two parts would be fused into one and that the flame — that is, the heat, the life, the spirit, of the contracting parties — would blend the two parts into a common cause.

When the sun was going down, a deep sleep fell upon Abraham; and lo, the mystery of darkness fell upon him. And it came to pass that, as the sun went down and it was dark, he dreamed he saw a smoking furnace, and a burning lamp that passed between the sacrificial pieces, and heard a voice which said,

Unto thy seed have I given this land, from the river of Egypt unto the great river, the river Euphrates. . . .[74]

A son to perpetuate his name, a homeland for his descendants — these promises, confirmed by age-old ceremonies, what more could a man ask of any Lord?

Meanwhile, the childless Sarah faced their problem from another angle. If Abraham was to have descendants to fulfill the Lord's promises, it appeared inevitable that Sarah must accept the common custom of their people and provide a second wife to bear his children. Legally, such children would be hers as well as the mother's, and Sarah's position as head of Abraham's household in no way would be challenged. So she chose a second wife for Abraham from among her handmaidens, the young girl she had brought back from Egypt, whose name was *Hagar.*

In spite of her good intentions, however, it displeased the nagging and outspoken Sarah to see Hagar enjoying the freedom of her new position in the family, and she complained to Abraham, saying, "I have given my maid to be thy wife, and now I am despised in her eyes."

But Abraham said:

. . . Thy maid is in thy hand; do to her as it pleaseth thee. And when Sarah dealt hardly with her, she fled from her face.

And the angel of the Lord found her by a fountain of water in the wilderness, by the fountain in the way to Shur.

And he said, "Hagar, Sarah's maid, whence camest thou? and whither wilt thou go?" And she said, "I flee from the face of my mistress, Sarah."

And the angel of the Lord said to her, "Return to thy mistress, and submit thyself under her hands. . . ."

And the angel of the Lord said unto her, "Behold, thou art with child and shalt bear a son, and shalt call his name Ishma-el [God hears]; because the Lord hath heard thy affliction. . . ."

And Hagar bare Abram a son: and Abram called his son's name, which Hagar bare, Ishma-el.[75]

21

Abraham and Ishmael and the Huluppu Tree

Abraham loved little Ishmael. He loved him as only a
father who has waited overlong for a son can love. He loved
him as the Arabs still love their sons: for the assurance he
gave that his father would not suffer the disgrace of dying
without a son to bury him and tend his grave. He loved him
for the promise of continuity Ishmael gave to the family
"name." He loved him for himself.

Although Ishmael's days were largely spent with the
women and children, it was a delight to Abraham, as the child
grew older, to have him to himself for little visits. At such
times, Abraham's thoughts sped in two directions: forward
into the years with Ishmael, and backward — for what reason
he knew not — into his own childhood. Then there came to
his lips legends and songs and stories he had known in the
long ago past.

"Did I tell you about the chaos dragon and how the world
was created?" he would ask his son; "did I tell you about the
Great Flood or the Tower unto Heaven that the gods destroyed?" And when he had told these stories again and again,
then he would say, "Did I tell you how Inanna, the queen of
heaven, got her throne and bed; did I tell you about Gilgamesh
and the Huluppu Tree?" [76]

"No," little Ishmael would cry out, "tell me about Gilgamesh and the Huluppu Tree and how the queen of heaven got
her throne and bed!"

And Abraham would begin.

"When heaven and earth had been separated and man
had been created, the god Anu took charge of heaven. The
god Enlil took charge of earth. And the god Enki set sail for
his dominion under the sea. The sea churned and foamed and

154

raged in honor of his passing, and the South Wind howled.

"On that day, a huluppu tree . . ."

"A what?" interrupted Ishmael.

". . . a huluppu tree — some people would call it a willow. On that day," continued Abraham, "a huluppu tree which had been planted on the bank of the Euphrates River and fed by its waters — on that day the huluppu tree was uprooted by the South Wind and carried off by the river. A goddess wandering on the river bank seized the floating tree, as she saw it passing, and brought it to the queen of heaven's garden in Erech.

"Here, Inanna, queen of heaven, herself tended the tree carefully and lovingly, thinking she would use its wood, when the tree was fully grown, to make a throne and a bed for herself.

"Ten years went by. Now the huluppu tree had grown. It was large enough to make a throne and a bed for even a goddess of heaven. So Inanna came to claim the tree.

"But alas! She could not cut it down because at its base the dragon, that snake that knows no charm, had set up for itself a nest. More than that, in the crown of the tree, a Zu-bird had a nest full of young. And, in the middle of the tree, Lilith, the demon goddess, had built herself a house!

"Then Inanna, the ever-shouting maid, the rejoicer of hearts, the pure Inanna, how she weeps!" On hearing this, Ishmael would laugh — and spur his father to even greater dramatic effort.

" 'When at last shall I have a holy throne that I may sit on it?' Inanna cried out; 'when at last shall I have a holy bed that I may lie on it?'

"The hero Gilgamesh heard her shouts of distress and rushed to her side. His mighty armor weighed as much as fifty mina: he treated its weight as if it had been thirty shekels! With his hefty ax — seven talents and seven mina, it weighed — with his hefty ax the giant Gilgamesh slew the dragon, the snake who knows no charm. This frightened the Zu-bird and she fled to the mountain with her brood. Lilith, too, the demon goddess, was terror-stricken; she tore down her house in the midst of the tree and escaped to the desert.

"Then the huluppu tree Gilgamesh plucked at its base like a flower. He tore at its crown. Unto the pure Inanna, goddess of heaven, for a throne he gave its wood, for a bed he gave it. From what remained of its base, for himself, his *pukku* he made; from what remained of its crown, for himself, his *mikkû* he made.

"So," Abraham would conclude, "Inanna, goddess of heaven, had her throne and her bed, and Gilgamesh had his *pukku* and his *mikkû!*"

Always Ishmael would ask, as now, "What was his *pukku*? What was his *mikkû*, Father?"

"Little one, there are some things too full of wonder to explain," Abraham would say, spreading his arms as if to encompass the world. "Look to the heavens, look to the earth, look to the sea! Can we explain them? Who paints protecting spots on the baby antelopes? Who tells the storks when to leave their snug nests and fly north?" His questions were a winch drawing Ishmael into the circle of Abraham's own wonderment, his own curiosity. "Who put the turquoise in the rock Eliezer gave you?" Abraham would demand. "How does the star get in the bottom of the well?"

Ishmael could not answer. With a willow twig, he was drawing a Zu-bird in the sand at their feet.

Continuing, Abraham would concede, "The *pukku* and the *mikkû* are not the same as these, but they are no easier to explain."

"But I want to know . . ."

And all Abraham could say was, "His *pukku* and his *mikkû* are wooden objects too full of magic to describe."

Suddenly, Ishmael was eager to see again the star reflected in their well. He jumped to his feet and ran from his father.

"Did I ever see a Zu-bird, Father?" he called back. not waiting for an answer.

22

"A Sign Upon Him That
He Is the Lord's"

In earlier times, primitive men had "bargained" with divine powers. In effect, they had said, "Do this for me, great invisible One, and I will do thus and so for you"; or, conversely, "See, Lord, what I am doing for you! I am anointing your image, I am sacrificing the first-born of my stock at your altar, I am leaving a little grain for you in the corner of my field — surely, you can do no less than grant my prayer!"

Did not the gods also bargain? the people asked. And was there not rivalry among the gods for the loyalty of mankind? "I am the god; choose *me* to follow and sustain!" "No, I!" "I." "Choose me!" "No, me!" they pictured the gods as saying. It was through bargaining and promises given and received, they thought, that men bound themselves to a favoring god and bound a favoring god to them.[77]

It was festival time in Canaan — time to give thanks to the Lord Baal for the fruits of the first harvest. (There were two harvests in Canaan, since barley ripened earlier than wheat.)

With sacrifice and song, Abraham's family had celebrated many a thanksgiving for its prosperity in Canaan. "Ask me anything, Lord, and I will give it you," had been Abraham's own constant cry, but not yet had the Lord god reciprocated the devotion and sent Sarah a son. Abraham had built altars in Canaan, and he had followed the Canaanite calendar of festivals. What else could he do, he wondered, to bind his family to the vast, unseen power that seemed so close to him, and he to the power, on Canaan's highest peaks?

To the Mesopotamians, An (Anu) had been the mystery of height, the god of space beyond the reach of man, the spirit of everything unknown. An was the first of Sumer's gods, the

157

earliest, the simplest of her deities. An was "height" before
ever settlers came to claim the flat delta marshes. An was
mystery; men broke that guileless mystery into petty gods with
man-made attributes, in man-made cities, and the immensity of
the mystery that "height" alone evoked was violated and dif-
fused.

Once a youth had stood on the stairs of the *ziggurat* at
Ur, intrigued by the "world" around him. Looking down, he
had seen the temples of Sumer's gods break the line of the
horizon. With never-ending wonder he had watched the
Euphrates River coming down from the mysterious mountains
of the north and winding its muddy way, like a slippery ser-
pent, between palm-bordered banks.

Now, man-grown, he stood on an Amorite peak, and again
his world spread round him. This was no man-made height
rising above shrines that dotted a flat Sumerian plain. He
was in the midst of mountains. Endlessly they stretched beyond
and above him; and to the west, not the muddy Euphrates, but
the blue waters of the Geat Sea.

He looked away from the long valleys that drained to the
coastal plains, and up to the colorful slopes of surrounding
peaks. How firm the mountains stood! How constant! Pulses
of strength, power, energy, and peace, which the mountains
contained, surged through his veins. The mystery of their
heartbeat was the mystery of his own. In them he felt secure.

While other men turned to the moon's light, the shadow
of rocks, the sanctity of caves, the bounty of water-holes, or
to the protection of river and sun, to find their manifestations
of God, more and more often Abraham found himself, as now,
lifting his eyes to the mountains and his heart to him whom the
Canaanites often called *el-Shaddai*, "the Mountain One." [78]

Suppose, here, suddenly, the god should direct him, saying, *I am el-Shaddai, the almighty, "the Mountain One," walk
before me and be blameless, and I will make my covenant* as a
promise *between me and you.*

So compelling was the thought and so vital the impact of
the suggestion, Abraham fell on his face in reverence, too overcome with emotion to stand. What more than he had already
done could he now do to influence the god who had blessed and

guided him these many years? By what further ceremony
could he bind an everlasting covenant between himself and his
family and the Lord Most High?

He remembered the flint knives that his people had sometimes found in the ground around some of the most ancient
shrines — knives so old they had been chipped from the rocks
and flaked to a cutting edge long before metal had come into
use. They had been used, the Canaanites told him, in an ancient sacrifice — the ceremony of circumcision.

"What had been the significance of the old ceremony?"
Abraham had wondered. The Canaanite priest could explain
only from hearsay because, at that time, the practice had lapsed
in Canaan.

"The sacrifice," he said, "brought a double blessing. It
bound members of the family or tribe everlastingly to each
other and to a god of their own choosing; and it bound the
god to them with promises of protection and of devotion to
their survival and well-being, through all their generations."

"It was better than sacrificing a life," another Canaanite
had added. "Like as not, it took the place of offering a human
being on the Lord's altar."

It would bind the Lord to a tribe through all generations,
Abraham repeated to himself. That was an assurance that appealed to him. Perhaps it was by a revival of such a ceremony
that he could persuade the Almighty One to become his god
forever. Then the Lord would know, and fulfill, Abraham's
desires.

Suppose the Lord should say, "I will make you the father
of nations, and kings shall come of you. I will give you the
land in which now you are a stranger, all the land of Canaan."

Suppose he should say, "I will bless Sarah and she shall
be the mother of nations. Sarah, your wife, shall bear a son
and you shall call his name *Isaac*." All this would happen!

The Lord would say, "I establish my covenant between you
and me and between your children after you for an everlasting
promise that I will be a god to you, and to your children after
you, in their generations. The covenant of circumcision shall
be upon your flesh as a token of the eternal promise between
you and the Lord god. Every man child among you shall be

circumcised; and whosoever is not circumcised, he has broken the covenant: he shall be cut off from the line of your people, for he will 'have no sign upon him that he is the Lord's.' "

Abraham was deeply moved. The promise did not seem too great. He remembered the bright spectacle of the rainbow in the heavens. The rainbow was said to be the sign of a pledge of god to man; circumcision, it appeared, was the sign of a pledge of man to god.

The festival of the first harvest was a momentous celebration for Abraham and his family that year. The Canaanites sang and danced and mimed as usual, extoling the invisible powers of vegetation. They recited classic words of praise and thanksgiving for the harvest. They feasted on the fruits of the land and the increase of their flocks. Abraham's family joined in this rejoicing: the Lord of the earth had quickened the seeds and provided the sunshine and rains as much for them as for the Canaanites; the barley had already fallen to the sickle and the swelling stalks of wheat gave promise of another reaping. It was a time for rejoicing. Nonetheless, for them, it was a solemn season and a proud occasion since, at the same time, Abraham and his people celebrated their first feast of circumcision and exchanged new promises, "for all their generations," with the Lord Most High. Then Abraham, the family priest, and "Ishmael, his son, and each of the men of his household, those born in his house, the slaves he had bought with gold, and all that were the sons of strangers, the foreigners he had that were not his children, and those bought with the money of any stranger" assembled, and each was circumcised as a token of alliance with each other and with the almighty God, and as "a sign upon him that he is the Lord's."[79]

23

The Lord's Messengers

As Abraham was sitting in the shade of the oak grove of Mamre, at the entrance of his tent, in the heat of the day, he lifted up his eyes and looked, and lo, there stood three men before him.

And as soon as he saw them, he ran from the entrance of the tent to meet them and bowed himself down to the ground, and said, "My lords, if now I have found favor in your sight, do not, I pray you, pass by your servant. Let now a little water be brought, that you may wash your feet, and rest yourselves under the tree; and let me bring a morsel of bread; afterwards you may pass on."

And they replied, "Do even as you have said." So Abraham hastened into the tent of Sarah, and said, "Make ready quickly three measures of meal, knead it, and bake cakes." Abraham also ran to the herd, and took a calf, tender and good, and gave it to the servant that he might prepare it quickly. And he took curds and milk, with the calf he had dressed, and set all these before them, and he waited on them under the tree, while they ate.

Then they said to him, "Where is your wife?" And he said, "There, within the tent." And they said, "Sarah thy wife shall have a son."

Sarah was listening at the entrance of the tent, which was behind him. And Sarah laughed, saying to herself, "Shall I, even when I am old, indeed bear a child?" And they said to Abraham, "Why did Sarah laugh: is anything too wonderful for the Lord?"

Then Sarah denied, saying, "I did not laugh"; for she was afraid. But they said, "Nay, but you did laugh."

Then the men rose up from there and looked in the direction of Sodom, . . . and Abraham went along with them to speed them on their way.[80]

The words of his uninvited guests were sweet to Abraham's ears. They gave one more assurance that he would have the son that he and Sarah longed for. Nor were the strangers' prophecies to be taken lightly: just as earlier peoples had feared that the gods of foreign nations were more powerful than their own, so, to people of Abraham's time, strangers at the gates of Canaan's cities suggested the presence of men more gifted, more farsighted, than themselves. Potentially, to them, every stranger could be a messenger of the Lord. Hospitality outdid itself lest, too late, a man discover he had been "entertaining angels unawares."

As strangers, these men were sometimes set apart in men's minds; set apart, they were credited with supernatural powers. The words of such guests were held to be as prophetic as those of the priests, if, upon leaving, they foretold the Lord's promise of imminent blessing or the Lord's warning of impending disaster.

Abraham was comforted by his guests' words.

But the pleasant promise of a child was not the only prophecy the Lord's messengers brought. They came to warn as well as to cheer.

As Abraham and his guests walked toward Sodom, they spoke of the plain ahead, where Lot had settled, and of the fame of its rich harvests and green pasture lands. They spoke, too, of the people of the cities of the plain.

"These city men forget the Lord," said one of the Lord's messengers. "When they have eaten of their plenty and are full, and their cattle wax fat upon the hills, they forget that the pasture lands, the wheat and the barley, the grapes and figs and pomegranates, and the oil and honey, all are the Lord's. 'It is my power and the might of my hand that has gotten me this wealth,' they say. But the Lord knows the measure of their waywardness!"

As they reached the height that overlooked the vale of Shittim, a pall of thin, grey haze hovered ominously over the valley and the smell of sulphur filled the air. There were places in the valley of Shittim where naphtha oozed from the ground, slimy and flammable. There was also asphalt (bitumen) for the gathering; it, too, was highly inflammable. Petroleum gases and light fumes of sulphur often hung on the air above the plain. But Abraham and the Lord's messengers had no thought of appraising Canaan geologically.

They had reached a position which overlooked the "garden of the Lord," the plain, the valley and the cities. It was time to part. But Abraham's guests had one last warning.

"The wickedness of the cities of the plain, by report, is great," one of the strangers continued. "Now the Lord will see for himself how grievous is their sin. And if it be as great as is the cry of it, the Lord will destroy Sodom and Gomorrah because of the wickedness of their people."

Then the men turned and went towards Sodom; but Abraham remained, and he pondered the words of the Lord's messengers. He thought of Lot, his brother's son, and members of Lot's family, living in Sodom. And his heart cried out,

"Surely the Lord will not destroy the righteous with the wicked! Peradventure there be fifty righteous men within the city, will he not spare the place for the fifty righteous that are within?" And he prayed to the Lord and said, "Shall not the judge of all the earth do right?"

He felt sure in his heart that if there were fifty righteous men to be found within the city of Sodom, the Lord would spare all for their sakes. With mixed emotions, Abraham struggled with his thoughts. Humbly he began his prayer, "I who am but dust and ashes . . ." and boldly he continued, "Peradventure there shall be lacking five of the fifty righteous within the city, will the Lord destroy it for lack of five?" Abraham knew his answers.

"If he find there forty and five, he will not destroy it."

"Or forty?"

"He will not destroy it for forty's sake."

"Oh, let not the Lord be angry if I speak again and say, If there be thirty . . . ?"

"He will not do it, if he find thirty there."

"Twenty?"

"And not for twenty's sake."

Still Abraham was not satisfied. "Oh, let not the Lord be angry if I speak but this once again: . . . for the sake of ten?"

"He will not destroy it for ten's sake."

And Abraham left off communing with the Lord and returned to Mamre. But the Lord's messengers had gone on to Sodom.[81]

When the strangers entered Sodom, Lot was reclining at

the city's assembly place. Immediately, he rose to meet these "angels unawares," and, with the hospitality due the stranger at the gates, bowed low before them.

"My lords," he said, "turn in, I pray you, to my house and tarry all night, and wash your feet; and you shall rise up early and go on your ways."

Lot's offer was according to the tenets of eastern hospitality; nor was the men's reply less formal or less customary.

"Nay, but we can abide in the street all night," they answered, knowing full well Lot would press his point.

Again Lot urged them to accept his invitation, and when they yielded and entered his house, he made them a feast and baked bread for them, and they ate with pleasure. Before any of them could lie down to sleep, however, Lot's house was ringed about by a crowd of noisy neighbors, curious as to who these travelers were whom Lot had appropriated to himself.

Lot was too newly come among the people of Sodom for them to accept such airs. He had left no opportunity for other men to have a chance to question the visitors. Even without prophetic powers, were not strangers always a source of news and story and hearsay from the outside world? Their presence belonged to all the men of a city: that was one of the attractions of the assembly place. The people of Sodom resented Lot's highhandedness, and the crowd increased — old men and young, from every quarter of the city.

They called out to Lot, shouting, "Where are the men who came in to you this night? Bring them out, that we may know them."

Lot went out and shut the door behind him and stood with his back to it. He argued with the men. "I pray you, neighbors, do not so wickedly. These men are strangers under my roof and I must needs take care of them." But the Sodomites would have none of his arguments.

"Stand back," they said. And they scoffed at Lot, the newcomer, saying, "This one fellow comes here to sojourn among us, and now he needs be a judge!"

"Stand back," they shouted. "Now we will deal worse with you than with the men inside!" And they pressed hard upon Lot, and came near to breaking the door.

Then the strangers put forth their hands quickly and pulled Lot into the house with them, and shut the door. Outside, darkness blinded the contenders until they could no longer find the door, and they wearied of their efforts.

The strangers inside came then to the point of their visit. "Have you here any beside yourself — sons, and daughters, and sons-in-law? Whatever you have in this city, bring out of this place. For we will destroy this city. Because the cry of Sodom is waxen great before the face of the Lord, the Lord has sent us to destroy it."

Lot went out and whispered to his sons-in-law, saying, "Up, get you out of here, for the Lord will destroy this city," but his sons-in-law paid no heed to his warning, for to them he seemed like one who jested.

When morning came the haze and the naphtha fumes lay like a grey pall upon the air. The strangers hurried Lot and said, "Arise, take your wife and your two daughters who are here, lest you all be consumed in the destruction of the city."

To Lot it all seemed too incredible to be true. For the moment he lingered, but the men laid hold of his hand, and his wife's hand, and the hands of his two daughters; and, being merciful to them, they led them out and directed them out of the city, and said, "Escape for your lives. Look not behind, neither stay you anywhere in the plain. Escape to the mountain, lest you all be consumed."

Still, Lot was not quite convinced. "Nay, say not so, my lords. I cannot escape to the mountain lest some evil overtake me and I die." From where they stood, in the distance ahead there was visible, beneath the haze, a little settlement of houses. Lot said, "Behold now, the town of Zoar is near to flee unto; and it is a little one. Its wickedness is not like that of Sodom. Let me escape thither — is it not a little one? — and my soul shall live."

"Haste you; escape thither," was all that the strangers could say.

The sun was risen upon the earth when Lot entered into Zoar.

Then the Lord rained upon Sodom and upon Gomorrah brimstone and fire from the Lord out of heaven.

And he overthrew those cities, and all the plain, and all the inhabitants of the cities, and that which grew upon the ground.

But his wife looked back from behind him, and she became a pillar
of salt.[82]

Remembrance of the disaster was long, as the memories
of the Flood in "the river country" had been. Men looked out
upon the scene of desolation where once the land had been
known as "the garden of the Lord." They were awed by the
gruesome pillars of salt standing ghostlike above the blackened
land, and, for generations, they asked, *Who did this? And why?*

They recalled the Sumerian story of the Tower of Babel [83]:
how the god himself had appraised the wicked ambitions and
intentions of Babel's people and, in anger, had confused the
workmen's speech and scattered the builders abroad lest, suc-
ceeding, their ladder reach to heaven and they become as gods.
And it seemed to them that the Lord, through his messengers,
again had come to earth — this time to appraise the wickedness
of the people of Sodom and Gomorrah, whose sins, they explained, must indeed have been great and "grievous before
the Lord" to have warranted such destruction. They could
find no other cause except the Lord Almighty's wrath at a
wicked people.

Geologists today, however, have a different explanation.
Some years ago they assumed that the disaster had been caused
by a volcanic eruption, but more recently it has been found
that Canaan's volcanic ruins are far older than Abraham's time
and that it was probably an earthquake that started Canaan's
holocaust.[84]

Although tremors of earthquakes were occasionally felt in
their country, the early people had no way of knowing that
through Canaan ran one of the great geological faults of the
earth's crust. A shift or depression in that crust was enough
to touch off an internal explosion of petroleum gases. The explosion must have sent tons and tons of flaming minerals —
asphalt, marl, salt, limestone — high into the air, which, when
it descended upon the plain and the people, appeared to be,
as they themselves described it, "brimstone and fire out of
heaven, from the Lord."

The earthquake, the explosion, and the fire followed so closely upon one another that they appeared as one blow to the bewildered people of Canaan who came from miles around to look upon, and mourn over, the devastation.

Traditionally, men linked this disaster with Abraham and Lot (and geologically the time agrees); and a new story was added to the Abraham cycle, *The Destruction of Sodom and Gomorrah.*

Abraham rose early in the morning and went to the place where, such a little time before, he had "stood before the Lord." He looked towards Sodom and Gomorrah and towards all the blackened land of the plain. The ruins of the cities stood black and gaunt in the southern hollow of the Salt Sea area, where waters of the sea soon began to overflow into the depression. A hill of salt, three miles wide and five miles long, stretched along the west side of the ruins and pillars of marl and salt, like silent witnesses, stood bleakly on the landscape. The "gardens of the Lord" were gone. Gone, too, was Lot's family. His wife, delaying, had been overcome by the holocaust; and Lot and his daughters had fled, first to Zoar and then northward to the mountain. The unhappy prophecy of "the Lord's messengers" had been fulfilled. Could he still count upon their happier promise? Abraham wondered.

So the seasons slipped away, and there was mourning in Canaan for many months. But when at last Sarah's child was born, neither Canaan's tragedy nor its mourning could dim the delight with which Abraham and Sarah beheld their long-desired son. Now Sarah would have less call to envy the motherhood of other women. The child was one more assurance — as Ishmael had been — that Abraham would have no need to plant an inscribed stone tablet in the wilderness, as other childless men must do, in order that his name should not perish from the face of the earth. All the songs of Canaan and all her rituals of thanksgiving were not enough to express the joy and gratitude Abraham's people felt for this, the Lord's greatest blessing, a son for Sarah and Abraham. Now they rejoiced in the covenant they had made with the Lord Most High.

Abraham named the child Isaac and circumcised him on the eighth day, as the Lord had commanded. And, again, Sarah laughed and was happy.

Nonetheless, a difficult relationship had been established, for now there were two mothers, Hagar and Sarah, and two sons, Ishmael and Isaac, in Abraham's immediate family.

24

Hagar and Ishmael

Before Isaac's birth, it had pained the childless Sarah to see Abraham and Ishmael and Hagar together, to hear them laugh and see the boy's eyes brighten in the presence of his father. True, it was Sarah who had decided, according to custom, which of her handmaidens should become the second wife. By custom, too, the child was hers as well as Hagar's.

Yet the fate of Ishmael and his maidservant mother was still in Sarah's hands according to the laws of her people. She had only to say the word and Abraham could not be excused from following her command. But Hagar's son was a stab in Sarah's heart.

When it came time for Sarah's own son to be weaned, Abraham made a great feast in celebration of Isaac's birth. The sight of Ishmael and his mother sharing the festivities displeased Sarah afresh, and she determined to get rid of them. Why should Hagar be allowed to sing and dance and revel in a household where Sarah's son had now been born to follow Abraham? So she said to Ishmael's father, "Drive out this maid and her son, for the son of my maidservant shall not be heir with my son, Isaac."

Grievous as the idea was to Abraham, because of Ishmael and because of Hagar, he knew that in all that Sarah had said he must concur, and that in Isaac his name would continue.

And Abraham rose up early in the morning, and took bread and a bottle of water, and gave it unto Hagar . . . and the child, and sent her away.[85]

Hagar had no choice but to obey. Yet, servant though she was and used to submission, she was stunned. Anger fed her dismay. Pride fanned her resentment. Tears shimmered like heat waves before her eyes, but she made her way out of Abraham's sight with a dignity he could not fail to observe. If, as she stumbled into the desert path, the gods and customs of the

169

Egyptian people were closest to her heart, it was small wonder, for Hagar had come from the south.

"O, mother of Egypt, sustain me," she prayed, casting about in her mind for some recourse which would save her and her child from a life of wandering, or worse.

In what had she erred since coming to Canaan? Had she so much as demurred at sharing her motherhood with this imperious Sarah whom, but for Sarah's nagging spirit, Hagar could have found it in her young heart to pity. Ishmael was Abraham's child, she had had to tell herself, and Sarah's according to the laws under which the family lived. She remembered, as the lad grew, how Abraham had loved Ishmael, played with him, told him stories. Her remembering turned to questioning, and her questioning to defiance.

Was Ishmael not still Abraham's son? What strange laws had these people brought with them to Canaan that allowed a wife to cast off her husband's child? Was Abraham's love of law greater than his love of his first-born son?

Day after day she and Ishmael followed the desert road, Hagar ever hoping they would meet a caravan of Egyptian traders who would consent to take them back to the land she had once so gayly left behind. As first the boy was curious, even eager, for what looked to him to be a new adventure. He had been brought up to obey, without question, whatever his father decreed. Even his mother's tears were not unfamiliar. Given a little time, Hagar could be counted on to regain her good nature. But no caravan came in sight.

The heat increased. Their food supply dwindled. Finally, they missed the road. Now they wandered without benefit of the water-holes and wells by which the road had been established.

In the distance, one evening, they heard the shouts and singing of a caravan passing, by the light of a waning moon, on the very road from which they had strayed, but by that time Ishmael had developed a desert fever and they had neither the strength nor the means to catch up with the travelers.

As the days passed, even shade was at a premium and the heat was unbearable. Now Ishmael no longer asked for food, only for water, water. So little water remained in the goatskin bottle — warm, tepid water, to be doled out drop by drop. Perhaps the water would last as long as the boy's need for it. And after that, Hagar cared no longer for her own life.

"Comfort, my little one," she said, parting Ishmael's hair with a motion that at the same time smoothed and shaded his fevered forehead from the afternoon sunlight. "Lean against my shoulder as you used to do when, as a baby, I sang you to sleep; and I will tell you of the wide, cool river that flows through far-away Egypt where the goddess Hathor, beside the Nile, watches over Egypt's baby kings."

Of sheer inertia, the lad suffered himself to be gathered into the circle of her loving arms. Nor was he conscious of the effort his mother must make so to enclose him, while waves of exhaustion swam before her eyes. Only the magic of re-membrance and the devotion of motherhood sustained her as, sick herself, Hagar struggled to comfort and encourage her child.

Suddenly, mercifully, she thought she was a little girl again, her father an Egyptian slave making bricks for the Pharaoh's newest temple. From a river barge, workmen were unloading a massive gilded and painted figure of the cow-goddess, Hathor. On the river bank, Hagar and her mother were watching the unloading, and her mother was telling her a story of the goddess Hathor. But before Hagar could even start to repeat the story of the goddess to Ishmael, Ishmael, in the solace of his mother's arms, was fast asleep.

Almost delirious from lack of food and water, it was no longer the gilt statue Hagar thought she saw, but the goddess Hathor herself, an oversized, mild-eyed cow standing among the lush papyrus plants on the river's edge. Between the cow's feet, floating in the water and half-hidden in the papyrus stalks, was a reed basket made waterproof with pitch; and in the basket, a baby, Hagar's baby, whom the divine bovine was promising Hagar she would guard and suckle as she had guarded and suckled each of Egypt's royal sons since time began.

It was an old tradition that Hathor nursed Egypt's royalty; temples dedicated to the cow-goddess contained statues repre-senting the goddess standing with her feet in the reeds, guarding the basket with its precious cargo, or guarding the child itself standing between her feet.[86] Now, Hagar's Ishmael was just such a precious freight.

"Hathor, hear me," his mother prayed, rousing from her illusion, "and spare the child." So great her need, so desperate her plight, Hagar forgot that not so long ago Abraham had sacrificed to the Lord god in Canaan and named his boy Ishma-el, meaning *God hears*.

The water in the bottle was gone, and Ishmael still tossed and turned and cried out with thirst. Her own burning throat was as nothing. For days she had tasted the grit of drifting dust between her teeth, but she was conscious only of her child's need.

Hagar had reached the end of her resources. Disdained by her mistress, cast off by her son's father, forgotten by her companions, her position seemed hopeless.

"Ishmael, Ishmael!" her heart repeated, with the sad monotony of a Bedouin's lullaby. "Ishmael! Ishmael!" And, like the echo of a distant song, the words came back to her, *God hears! God hears!*

Something stirred in Hagar's mind. Was it the whisperings of an angel, as men in later days were wont to say? She sat up, easing Ishmael's head to her lap. She turned her face to the blazing sun that only a moment ago had seemed so hostile. Did she remember now the powers of Egypt's sun-god? And did the thought come to her that Re-Atum crossed the sky daily to bring *life* not death, to all mankind?

Hope quickened her returning consciousness. Pride sustained her. She might be scorned by her mistress, cast off by her master, forgotten by the whole of Canaan, but suddenly her faith in a divine Comforter was greater than her bereavement.

"*God hears! God hears! Ishmael,* my beloved."

For the first time, she saw her son not as the child disdained by Sarah, but as the man he might yet grow to be: son of Abraham, a leader of free men; a free man himself; and the father of free men. His was a heritage not to be despised. Prayer rose to her lips, but the lord she prayed to was not Egypt's, was not Canaan's. It was hers, Hagar's; born of despair and hope, this God peculiarly her own, whose "angel" now directed her!

She eased the sleeping Ishmael to the ground and stood up, feeling strangely refreshed and able to do something about their needs. With one backward glance at the boy, she walked to the top of a little ridge of land beyond which she had watched birds making lazy circles all day. Sure enough, on the other side of the ridge, a trickle of water coughed its way out of the hillside and watered a green path down the slope. At the foot of the slope were berries, warm and sweet from the sun's heat. Quickly Hagar splashed her hands and face with the life-giving water and filled the goatskin bottle which hung limply from her shoulder. With fingers that trembled she gathered a handful of berries to take back to Ishmael as a promise of more to come. And beyond the berry bushes, having been obscured before by the ridge of land, she saw a stretch of the highway itself and, in the distance, a caravan unloading its tents and building fires and preparing to camp on the road's further side. Seeing these preparations, Hagar knew that the travelers would not immediately depart.

The sun was sinking in the west as she finished bathing and feeding Ishmael, and the evening breeze was stirring when Ishmael, refreshed, gave evidence of returning health.

Now the sickle of a pale, new moon renewed the promise of that endless cycle of life of which Hagar and Ishmael were each a vital part. Still, it was not Harran's moon-god, or Egypt's sun-god, or Canaan's Baal, nor Hathor, royalty's divine nurse — or was it all of them together — that led Hagar and Ishmael across the ridge to the security of the caravan's desert hospitality.

"God hears, God hears!" was the song that sang in Hagar's heart.

regarded a generation or two ago.[87] One wonders just what historical experience in the life of Abraham could have been the kernel out of which the poignant legend of the Sacrifice of Isaac grew, and whether the tradition stemmed from Abraham's own time or was the work of a later author who was trying to convince his people that God did not care for human sacrifice.[88]

Inconsistent though human sacrifice may seem to be with all Abraham's other relations with his son, it is still possible that, threatened by some dire calamity to his tribe or frantic because of the spread of some fatal epidemic, Abraham could not resist the pleadings of his people to do something that would assuage God's anger. Their prayers and the sacrifice of the best of their herds and flocks had been of no avail: the scourge continued to take its awful daily toll of life. What else could be done? they asked, and looked to Abraham for the answer.

We do not know what harrowing emergency may have brought to Abraham's mind the thought of this supreme and ultimate sacrifice of the ancient world. Perhaps it was a stubborn threat of grave disaster that confronted his people. Perhaps it was a personal, poignant test of his devotion to el-Shaddai, as tradition has said.

And it came to pass . . . that God did prove Abram, and said unto him, . . . "Take now thy son, thine only son, whom thou lovest, even Isaac, and get thee into the land of Moriah; and offer him there for a burnt offering upon one of the mountains which I will tell thee of." And Abram rose up early in the morning, and saddled his ass, and took two of his young men with him, and Isaac his son, and he clave the wood for the burnt offering. . . .[89]

There was a fierce doggedness in the persistence with which Abraham directed the young men to load the resinous, sacrificial wood upon the asses, but the lines of Abraham's face softened once the party was on its way.

Always, the mystery of the mountains' purple tops was a magnet drawing him in spite of himself. It was a goal as much to his spirit as to his feet. By the time he had reached their foothills and was, himself, within the mountain range, the vision — and the goal — leveled off; until, reaching the peak and looking back upon the land, he was no longer stalking the mystery: he was part of it.

So it was, again. Northward, the mountains rose before him, looming high at first and then appearing to shrink and level off as the little party reached the foothills that led to Uru-salem, and came, on the third day, to the particular mound that Abraham sought.

Abraham said to the young men, "Stay here, while Isaac and I go yonder to worship." Then he took the wood and laid it on Isaac's shoulder. He took the burning knot he had saved from their campfire. He took the knife with which he had provided himself. His shoulders were bent, and there was a fiery ardor in his troubled eyes that seemed to mark the occasion as a ritual of far more importance than any ordinary ceremony.

Isaac said, "Here is the fire and the wood, but where is the lamb for the burnt offering?"

"God will provide the offering," Abraham answered, without looking up.

The young men could only blink with astonishment, for suddenly they knew that Abraham was about to offer his son Isaac as a human sacrifice to the Mountain God, el-Shaddai. They would have cried out in protest except for their life-long training in trusting Abraham's judgment without question. They looked at each other in awe: not in their lifetime had they witnessed the ancient rite.

Soon father and son disappeared through a gap above them — Abraham, white-haired, a heavy man, his broad shoulders bent with the weight of his intention, and Isaac, agile, ready to obey his father's least command — and the young men waited for the smoke that would signalize the sacrificial fire. One of them rose in protest in spite of his training, only to be held back by the other; but in a matter of moments it was the other who was being restrained from the same impulse.

The smoke rose and the smell of the sweet woods that had kindled the fire filled the air. The young men lay down to await Abraham's return, understanding Abraham's motive no more than they understood the voices of the birds around them.

When Abraham returned to the young men, he was not alone. Isaac was with him. They jumped to their feet, their faces ashen with suspense.

"But we . . ." they stammered, and were still.

Abraham realized their confusion.

"Praise be to el-Shaddai, the almighty, 'the Mountain One,'" was his happy greeting. And he told them what had happened; how he

. . . came to the place which God had told him of; and Abram built an altar there, and laid the wood in order, and bound Isaac, his son, and laid him on the altar upon the wood. And Abram stretched forth his hand, and took the knife to slay his son. And the angel of the Lord called unto him out of heaven, and said, . . . "Lay not thine hand upon the lad, neither do thou anything unto him; for now I know that thou fearest God, seeing that thou hast not withheld thy son, thine only son, from me." And Abraham lifted up his eyes, and looked, and beheld behind him a ram caught in a thicket by his horns: and Abraham went and took the ram, and offered him up for a burnt offering in the stead of his son. . . . And the angel of the Lord called unto Abraham . . . the second time, and said, ". . . By myself have I sworn . . . because thou hast done this thing, and hast not withheld thy son, thine only son, that in blessing I will bless thee, and in multiplying I will multiply thy seed as the stars of the heaven, and as the sand which is upon the sea shore; . . . and in thy children shall all the nations of the earth be blessed, because thou hast obeyed my voice." [90]

The man who walked down from Mount Moriah with his son by his side had demonstrated his unswerving and unbounded faith in the Lord God, and become the symbol of faith for all time — the "Father of the Faithful." The Lord had provided the offering and Abraham's faith had been justified. His relief was tremendous. The Lord on High could accept his devotion, but not his method of proving it. Isaac's life, not his death, was what the Lord wanted — a life that, in living, would make Abraham's people a blessing to mankind.

Abraham's feet had not faltered as he climbed the mountain to tender his most extreme loyalty to el-Shaddai; but now, and for the next few years, his step had in it a new springiness and a livelier gait, as if the weight of a pressing obligation had been lifted and a great burden laid down. Perhaps he had

planned the supreme sacrifice not merely as a propitiation during a crisis; but to prove — to himself, to his people, and to his
god — that not even the love of his long-awaited son could
come before his devotion to the Lord Most High.

26

The Silver Boat Sails

So the seasons came and went in Canaan until a day arrived when, alone, Abraham stood in the high valley of Mamre — more humble, more beaten in spirit than he had ever been in all his years. For Sarah, his wife, was dead.

Death was not new to Abraham. Death was necessary. It was natural. It was inevitable. In Ur he had helped to bury his brother, Lot's father. In Harran he had buried Terah. Then he could say, as was the custom, "He is gone; the Lord have mercy upon him." Now it was Sarah, his wife, who had gone from him. And it was not the same.

He lifted his face to the mountains above him with an intensity born of defeat. Soon he must return to his waiting household, but first he craved to lean upon the great invisible power whose beauty and strength had never failed him. Quietly, he prayed:

O, God Most High, All-mighty One, who makest the hinds to calve, who discoverest the forests and levels the plains, who causest the mountain to shake, and who sittest upon the flood, Thy wrath lies hard upon me.

Thou hast afflicted me with all thy waves of sorrow.
Mine eye mourneth by reason of affliction, and my soul is full of trouble.

Lord, daily have I called upon thee with the fruits of the land;
Yet I am afflicted and ready to die. Lover and companion thou hast taken from me, and mine acquaintance thou hast put into darkness.

Shall thy loving-kindness be declared in the grave?
Or thy faithfulness be shown in destruction?
Shall thy wonders be known in the dark? Or thy righteousness in the land of forgetfulness?

Lord God Most High, Great Mountain,[91] why hidest thou thy face from Abraham, thy servant? [92]

180

There was a field in Mamre, with oaks and at the far end a cave. It belonged to Ephron the Hittite, son of Zohar. Abraham craved the cave for a family sepulcher, since he had no place, in this new homeland, in which to bury his wife.

He went to the gate of the town where Canaanites and Hittites, and men of all the other nationalities in Mamre, gathered daily to do business. In Mamre, as in other towns and cities of the time, an open area near the entrance was set aside for holding public assemblies, for buying and selling, and as a place for social intercourse in general. It was more than a market place. It was the center of communal life. Here law courts convened, trials were held, contracts entered into, public announcements made; and here strangers having no other place to sleep could spend the night. At sunset the gate was closed, but in the daytime the area around the gate was the threshold and the key to everything that happened in Mamre.

Abraham moved among these people as a new friend and with a dignity increased by grief. Often he had visited the gate and listened to other mens requests. Now it was he who came asking, and the curious and sympathetic gathering made way for him and his demands. The population of Mamre being largely Hittite, Abraham stood before the audience at the gate and said, "Children of Heth, I am a stranger and a sojourner with you, and I have no burying-place. Give me the possession of a burying-place with you, that I may bury my dead out of my sight."

The crowd murmured feelingly, and a Hittite answered the rich Abraham, saying, "Hear us, my lord, you are a mighty prince among us. Take your choice of any of our sepulchers in which to bury your dead," and the audience appeared to assent. The proud Abraham stood and bowed to the people gathered at the gate of the town, even to the Hittites, "the children of Heth," whom Sarah had despised. No one of them intended him to accept the offer, and Abraham knew it; this was their Oriental way of saying he was welcome to a burying-place in their land.

The next step in the Oriental pattern of bargaining — and the pattern exists to this day — was for Abraham to name the site he had in mind.

"Seeing you are willing that I bury my dead amongst you, entreat for me with Ephron, the son of Zohar," he said, "that he may give me the cave of Machpelah, which he has at the end of his field. For as much money as it is worth, ask him to give it to me for a burying-place amongst you."

With great formality, Ephron the Hittite rose from among the crowd and bowed to the rich Abraham and said, in a voice loud enough for all his fellow Hittites and the rest of the audience at the gate to hear, "Nay, my lord, hear me: I give you the field and the cave that is in it; in the presence of the sons of my people I *give* it to you; bury your dead." The bargain was not over, and Abraham said exactly what Ephron expected him to say: "If you will give it, I will give you money for the field; take my money and I will bury my dead there."

With feigned indifference, Ephron then mentioned the sum he had had in mind all the time. "My lord," he answered, "the land is worth four hundred shekels of silver, but" — with a further show of nonchalance — "what is that between you and me? Bury your dead."

Abraham heard what Ephron the Hittite had said and, in the presence of the audience gathered at the gate of Mamre, he weighed out the price, "four hundred shekels of silver, current money with the merchant." Now it was time for Abraham to be specific and to name the details of the transaction in the presence of witnesses at the gate; and this he did.

And the field of Ephron, which was in Machpelah, . . . the field, and the cave which was therein, and all the trees that were in the field, that were in the borders round about, were made sure unto Abraham for a possession in the presence of the children of Heth, before all that went in at the gate of the city.

And after this, Abraham buried Sarah his wife in the cave of the field of Machpelah before Mamre; the same is Hebron in the land of Canaan.[93]

When, at last, the burial rituals had been sung and the elaborate ceremonies were over, Abraham went home and saw another night descend upon his grief. How often he and Sarah had watched while the same canopy of stars expanded the joys they shared or belittled their trials!

Above him, the young moon was a silver boat pushing its way across the sky. Watching it, Abraham thought, like the ancient Sumerians, was it in such a boat that the wonder and vibrancy and dynamic personality — the spirit — of Sarah had departed? And would it return, and if so, *when?* to the pale, silent body they had so tenderly laid in the waiting cave within the shadow of the oaks of Mamre? Or did the wonder and the vibrancy and spirit of Sarah's body linger only in the hearts of those who had loved her?

Shall thy wonders be known in the dark? Or thy righteousness in the land of forgetfulness?

Lord God Most High, Great Mountain, why hidest thou thy face from Abraham, thy servant?

27

A Wife for Isaac

Night after night, the "silver boat" increased in size and shape until, by the time its full face claimed the scene, the moon was to Abraham no longer the mysterious symbol of Sarah's passing, but a call back to reality. Before the month was over, Abraham and Isaac had returned to their harvestings and threshings and all the other occupations that the late evening breeze and the light of a brilliant moon made possible in the coolest part of the day. But nothing was the same.

Something was lacking in their lives. Without Sarah, their home was barren. Nor was there even the solace of emptiness and monotony one might have expected following her death, since, without Sarah's guiding hand, the servants were restless and argumentative. There were rivalries and quarrels to be resolved and bickerings to be suppressed.

It was a wife for Isaac that the family needed, a woman who could follow in Sarah's footsteps and care for Isaac and Abraham and comfort them in their bereavement. Then the work would be properly assigned and the needs of the group anticipated and met. And once again there would be laughter and forbearance and a happy home! *God's peace*, Abraham's nomadic ancestors would have called it.

That Isaac should choose a wife among the Canaanites was to his father unthinkable. Mesopotamia was the family homeland: surely among their relatives and friends in the Balikh valley there was a girl as worthy and capable as Sarah had been. Someone would have to find and fetch such a girl. There was only one man to whom Abraham would entrust this delicate mission — Eliezer, his household steward, growing old now in Abraham's service.

Abraham had scarcely realized how many domestic questions had been settled by Sarah with tact and good judgment.

184

He had assumed that most of the family problems had come
to him to be solved. The violent ones, at least, had been his.

Abraham's decisions, whether gentle or firm, were softened
by the underlying humanity of his words: "I am thy father; I
am thy brother . . . and my judgment is thus and my com-
mandment so and so."

Whether the disputes arose between rough herdsmen at
the watering holes or between the more favored clansmen,
arguing, as they sat together drinking sweet *leban* in their
comfortable tents, Abraham was arbiter and peacemaker of his
people, and "father" to them all.

As a title of reverence, "my father" was not required always to denote a blood kinship.

"I am thy father," "I am thy brother," ". . . thy sister,"
"I am thine uncle's son," were words that tied the clan into
one self-centered whole, strong and cohesive in the face of
outside aggression. It tied its people, too, to relatives in other
parts of their world: they were all "brothers" for generations.

Safety, security, justice, and wisdom his people found in
Abraham's words, "I am thy father." Safety, security, justice,
and wisdom had a wider meaning for Abraham, and his search
for them culminated sublimely in "I am the Lord thy God."
Whatever the Lord god ordained would be right: it was the
Lord's will.

Abraham called Eliezer to him and told his steward that
he must go to Mesopotamia, to the city of Abraham's brother
Nahor, in search of a wife for Isaac. He made Eliezer swear
that Isaac's wife would be chosen from within their own family
and never from among the foreign populations of Canaan.

"But if, perchance, the maiden will not come with me,"
asked Eliezer, "shall I not return and bring Isaac back with me
to Harran?"

"Isaac's place is here," his master answered. "If the maiden
refuses to return with you, you shall be thereby relieved of
your oath."

The arrangements for the trip were for Eliezer to make.
As steward, he knew what men and what supplies would be
needed. As steward, too, he knew of what treasures he could

avail himself in Abraham's name — jewels and fabrics and weapons and beautifully wrought household appurtenances that would charm the young woman and her family and give evidence of his master's status as a wealthy man.

Eliezer and his men and his well-laden animals made a relatively comfortable journey over roads that were somewhat more crowded with commerce than they had been when Abraham's caravan came to Canaan. There were few landmarks to remind Eliezer of the day when they had left Nahor's village amidst festive rites and cries of *God speed*.

Eliezer had sworn before Abraham to give his best efforts to his mission. But the nearer he came to Harran, the less certain he felt of his success. How, indeed, would he find the young woman? How would he persuade her to come with them? As he made his way northward into the Balikh valley, he could only believe, as Abraham did, that all things were in the hands of the Lord.

It was exciting to reach Nahor's village. And here, the watering place, at least, was familiar. Yet he approached it with misgivings, praying that the Lord would help him recognize the bride his master had sent him so far to find. Many women, young and old, came to fill their jugs and pitchers at this well.

"Lord God of my master Abraham," Eliezer prayed, "if you would continue to prosper my way, let it come to pass that the young woman to whom I shall say 'Let down your pitcher that I may drink,' and she shall say 'Drink, and I will water your animals as well' — that woman shall be she whom you have appointed as a wife for your servant Isaac. Thereby shall I know your kindness to my master Abraham."

Almost before he had finished his prayer, a young woman, very fair to look upon, with a pitcher on her head, went down to the edge of the well to draw water. She filled her pitcher and was returning when Eliezer asked, "I pray you, let me drink a little water from your pitcher."

With a graceful sweep of her arms, she lowered the heavy pitcher. "Drink, my lord, and I will bring water also for your animals." When Eliezer had finished drinking she emptied her pitcher into the trough provided for the animals, then ran to the well, filling and emptying her pitcher into the trough until the asses had done drinking.

Eliezer watched her movements with satisfaction and hope. She wore a simple, indigo-dyed, blue smock, its hem and loose sleeves enlivened by a design of multicolored patches. A soft kerchief covered her hair. She was tall and fair, with that freshness that lingers briefly between childhood and maturity.

Not for nothing had Eliezer hung a small bag of little treasures around his neck inside his tunic. From it he drew a golden ring of half a shekel's weight — a nose ring, in that country where every woman's nose was pierced for ornaments. More than that, two bracelets for her hands — of ten shekels' weight of gold they were and valuable to say the least — these also he produced. Then he gave the ring and the bracelets to her, saying, "Whose daughter are you? And is there room in your father's house for us to lodge there overnight?"

She answered proudly, "I am Rebekah, the daughter of Bethuel, the son of Nahor. We have both straw and provender enough for your animals and room for you and your men to lodge."

Eliezer could only say, "Blessed be the God who has led me to my master's brethren."

The girl ran ahead of him to tell her mother what had happened at the well, and Laban, her brother, came out to meet and greet the strangers. He had heard what his sister had said. He had seen the rich presents Eliezer had given her.

"Blessed of the Lord, come in," he said. "Why stand you outside? We have prepared the house for you and have room for your animals." Eliezer and his men entered the house, while willing hands unloaded, fed, and bedded down the asses.

Water was brought to wash the men's feet. There was meat to feast the strangers. But before Eliezer would so much as taste his host's food, he must make an honest explanation of his purpose.

"I will not eat until I have told my errand," he said, and Laban answered, "Speak on."

Then Eliezer said, "I am Abraham's servant. In the years since he left Harran, the Lord has blessed my master exceedingly. He has become great. The Lord has given him flocks and herds, and silver and gold, and manservants and maid-servants in great number, and asses as well as cattle and sheep."

He told them of Isaac's birth and of Abraham's concern for his favorite son and his desire that Isaac should not marry outside the circle of Terah's family.

"'Go to my father's house and to my kindred in Mesopotamia,' he told me, 'and there take a wife for Isaac my son.' And he made me swear an oath that Isaac should not marry among the daughters of Canaan. 'Peradventure, the woman will not follow me; what then?' I asked my master. He answered, 'The Lord before whom I walk will direct and prosper your way, and you shall take a wife for my son of my kindred, and of my father's house. But if, when you come to my kindred, they will not give you one of their daughters, then you shall be clear of the oath you have sworn to me this day.'"

Then Eliezer related how he had come to the village well, praying in his heart that the Lord would direct him, and of how he had, at that very moment, met Rebekah. He told of her kindness to him, a stranger, and to his animals.

"'Whose daughter are you?' I asked. And she said, 'The daughter of Bethuel, Nahor's son.'" His audience could not fail to be impressed. There was more than coincidence to such a meeting, in their opinion.

"Then I put the ring upon her face, and the bracelets upon her hands, and I bowed my head and worshiped the Lord and blessed the God of my master Abraham, who had led me in the right way to take my master's brother's daughter to his son."

Eliezer leaned back and paused to let the full flavor of his story permeate the thoughts of his listeners. He finished his tale by asking, "Now if you will deal kindly and truly with my master, tell me; and if not, tell me; in order that I may know if I turn to the right hand (success) or to the left (failure)."

Then Bethuel and Laban answered: "This thing cometh from the Lord: we cannot answer for it, *Yes* or *No*. Behold, you have found Rebekah; take her and go, and let her be Abraham's son's wife, for the Lord has spoken!"

At their words, Eliezer bowed in thankfulness. He took from his luggage "jewels of silver and gold, and raiment, and gave them to Rebekah; he gave them also to her brother and many precious things to her mother."

Only then did Eliezer and his men eat and drink. They slept at Bethuel's house and rose up in the morning impatient to be off. Eliezer said to his host, "Bless my journey and send me away to my master." Rebekah's mother and brother protested at his haste, asking that Rebekah be given a little time, "ten days at least, and after that she shall go." But Eliezer cried, "Hinder me not, since the Lord directs my way."

"We will call Rebekah and enquire of her."

"Will you go with this man?" they asked. And Rebekah answered, "I will go."

With formality, they sent them away — Rebekah, their daughter and sister, with her nurse and servants, and Abraham's steward and his men. And they blessed Rebekah and wished her well, saying, "You are still our sister; be you the mother of thousands."

Rebekah and her women mounted the asses provided for their journey and followed Abraham's men. And Eliezer, having found a wife for Abraham's son, turned back to Canaan.

Meanwhile, in the South Country of Canaan, Abraham and Isaac waited for word of the success or failure of Eliezer's mission. There had been no thought of Isaac going to Mesopotamia to choose a wife for himself. Nor, in those days, would a son have questioned his father's rights in deciding this matter. Still, Isaac must have been curious as to his future bride.

One evening, Isaac went out in the field as was his habit. In that hot country, it was the cool and vibrant part of the day. Meditating on many things, and thinking no doubt of Eliezer and his journey, Isaac looked up and saw at a distance the very caravan he had in mind. The travelers saw him, too.

"What man is this that walks in the field to meet us?" Rebekah asked.

"It is my master, Isaac."

Rebekah lighted off her mount, holding tightly in her hands the veil that etiquette demanded. Her heart was pounding like the hammer of the goldsmith beating his gold, yet, to all outward appearance, she waited for Isaac to come up to her, as poised and confident as a young hind in its native wilderness.

She was tall, and freshly clad.[94] The veil she lightly held against her face covered little more than her mouth and chin. A gold nose ring with tiny, coin-shaped pendants hung from her right nostril. Nor did the veil conceal her grace of body. Over her saffron-colored robe, a tiny girdle of gay scarlet lace encircled her slender waist.

Eliezer stood beside his master and this fair young bride.

"This is my master Isaac, the son of your father's brother — Abraham's son, who seeks your hand in marriage."

Isaac, looking down on the beautiful young stranger, so far from her native homeland, said gently, "And what is your mind in the matter, my sister?"

She looked up into the face of the strong, kindly man whom she had come those many miles to marry and answered, quaintly, with calm confidence, "If you will but receive me, kinsman, I am willing."

Barefoot, all her bracelets and charms and little pendants jingling as she moved, she followed Isaac across the sun-warmed field now cooling under the evening breeze. Beautiful, erect, was her grace. Together, the three found Abraham.

Meanwhile, in Sarah's tent, Rebekah's servants unpacked her wedding finery.

28

Isaac, Man of the Field

The years passed swiftly following Sarah's death and Isaac's marriage, until there was no one left among his people who could remember Abraham as a young man. A few could recall Isaac's birth but, one by one, their number grew smaller. Now Isaac had two sons of his own, *Esau* and *Jacob* (who was also called *Isra-el*). And Abraham was an old man.

As long as any of them could remember, Abraham had been the light that guided his family — dependable, steady, strong. In the comfortable assurance of that light, his people had gone their way, abiding by Abraham's decisions, confident of Abraham's ability to "show the way." Small wonder that in more ancient days often such ancestors were remembered as little less than gods!

Now the light that was Abraham grew dim, but the shadow lengthened. In it something of Abraham remained: a shadow never quite obliterated, cast by a new light, it too a little paler — Isaac. So little information concerning Isaac was passed down by oral tradition that he stands out far less vividly than his father, Isaac's story often repeating exploits already credited to Abraham.

Isaac was more than a shadow, however, and more than an historical link between his father and his sons. No man could have guided that large, turbulent, prosperous "family" through another generation without having strong powers of leadership and deep reservoirs of faith. Yet, it is in the perspective of others — his father, his mother, his wife, and his twin sons — that Isaac comes to life. Except through them, and in relation to his times, his story must remain imaginative.

We like to think that Isaac's gentleness and serenity of spirit were fostered by association with his father, yet Abraham and Isaac appear to have been quite different in temperament. It could well have been that Abraham's idealism confused Sarah's son.

When Isaac stood under a moonlit sky, he was not consciously drawing inspiration from the moon-faith of his forebears, as Abraham might have been; he was making a keen appraisal of the weather. He was "noting the position of the stars for signs of rain" and plotting his seedtime and harvest in relation to the phases of the moon. He was listening for a harbinger of spring in the turtledove's first plaintive notes and for a weather forecast in the tree toad's monotonous croak.

His powers of natural observation were even sharper, perhaps, than his father's. Neither man would have missed the bay of a wolf, the threat of a jackal, or the warning of a screech owl; but Isaac found music in the bleat of a newborn lamb, in the sound of a partridge drumming, and in the "bob-white" of the quail. He knew the slopes that led to green pastures. He "sniffed the wind" for water. Weather-wise, he knew the meanings of bright dawns and brilliant sunsets, of mackerel skies and rings around the moon.

Abraham would have found, in the first unexpectedly-warm day of Spring, a bright reiteration of that promise of life and light that men had been waiting for ever since the winter solstice. But Isaac saw in it a hope that the lambing season would be warm.

Breathing the pungent, earthy odors that rose from the moist and pregnant ground, Abraham's sense of well-being expanded. Its fragrance pulsed through his veins like new blood, crying *Faith, faith, faith!* — faith of long ages to which he was heir, faith in the present through the favor of the Lord Most High, and faith in the future of his "house" as assured through Isaac.

But the same odors, no less welcome, no less satisfying to Isaac, spoke a different language to Sarah's son. On the same spring morning, he would have appraised the condition of the first sprouts of the family's fall sowings; and in the evening, reached for his bow and quiver and gone hunting.

Isaac knew the haunts of the antelope and the water-holes of the fleet gazelle and where to wait, concealed, for a shot at a wild boar. He knew the glades in which the roebuck *yarded* and the season of the year when their flesh was firm and sweet to eat. He knew how to spread a net for wild pigeons and how to trap with bait the animals that hid from his arrow. But the responsibilities for family leadership which Abraham enjoyed had less appeal than these pursuits to Abraham's son.

For Isaac was, as his son Esau would also be, ". . . a cunning hunter, a man of the field," who "loved Esau because he did eat of his venison."

29

Fulfillment

Abraham was an old man:[95] both Life and Death now walked with him as friends. His experiences had been wide and varied over the years. They had taken him into several countries, each with its own interpretation of God. He had offered sacrifices to Terah's *moon-god* in the high temples of Sumer and Mesopotamia and to the unnamed family god in the lowly chapel of his home. He had joined his Canaanite neighbors in propitiating Canaan's *Lord of the Earth* and, amid Canaan's mountains, he had built his own shrines to the Lord Most High, *el-Shaddai.* He had shared the bounty of Egypt with men who looked to the sun and the river to symbolize the Creator and Guide of mankind. And he had returned to the hill country of Canaan awed by the majesty and power of the Lord God Almighty everywhere. What he had longed for and worked for and prayed for, he had seen come to fruition. He had cast off Ishmael but now, with Sarah gone, this son, grown to manhood, often visited his father. And, following Sarah's death, he had married Keturah. Once, he had craved, above all else, a son in order that his name would not perish from the earth. Now, he had sons and grandsons.

If thou canst count the stars in heaven, so shall your children be numbered: how bountifully, with the years, had the Great Creator assured him of descendants. Now Abraham prayed that, in this land to which he had come as a stranger, the Lord would prosper those descendants and be their god forever.

Feeling that his death would not be delayed for long, Abraham called all his people together for that final blessing which was to them as much a forecast of the future as a ritual of farewell. When Death approached and a man's spirit was hovering between the visible and invisible worlds, it was commonly thought that his words would be weighted with a divine wisdom and vision. Such prophecy was a benediction none but the dying could bestow.

When his great family was assembled, Abraham blessed all the important things in his sons' and grandsons' lives — their land, the rain and dew, their seedtimes and harvests, the labor of their hands, their children, and their herds and flocks. Then, as was the custom, he prophesied the future of each one according to what he knew of his individual skills and temperament, and gave each one a gift. And he enjoined them all to make sacrifices to their God on High.

After the blessing and the gifts, and after the feasting and the songs that accompanied this solemn reunion, he directed Ishmael and his family to return to the south, to the *Negeb*, and the sons of Keturah and their sons to settle beyond the borders of Canaan, eastward. Then the assembly dispersed and his "children" went their separate ways.

Death waited for some weeks longer, however; and Ishmael and Isaac and their families had time to return to celebrate the feast of the first fruits of the harvest with their father. It was to have been a seven-day festival and a happy occasion for them all.[96]

Rebekah, Isaac's wife, made cakes of the newly gathered grain and, since Abraham was too feeble to take a more active part in the festivities, she gave some of them to her son Jacob, Abraham's favorite grandson, for him to carry to Abraham in his tent. By Jacob Isaac, also, sent drink made from the first fruits of the land for a thank-offering, in order that his father might "eat and drink and bless the *Creator of all* before he died." Then Abraham ate and drank and said,

"Blessed be the Most High God, Creator of heaven and earth, who has made all the fat of the earth and given it to the children of men, to eat and drink, in order that they should bless their Creator."

To Jacob, his favored grandson, Abraham said, "Fear not for the future, my son Jacob, and do not tremble, son of Abraham: the Lord God Almighty will protect you from all destruction, and from all the paths of error he will deliver you. . . . And your children and your name will endure in all the generations of the earth."

Then the night came. Jacob slept near his grandfather in Abraham's tent. Early, before the dawn, Jacob awoke and rose to look at his grandfather. He touched Abraham's face and found it cold.

"Father, Father," he said, but there was no answer, and he knew that Abraham was dead.

Then Jacob ran to tell his mother and she went to Isaac in the night and told him; and together Rebekah and Isaac and Jacob, with a lamp, went back to the tent where Abraham lay dead.

Isaac fell upon the face of his father Abraham and kissed him and wept; and his lamentations were heard throughout all "the house of Abraham." Ishmael also arose and came and wept over his father, "he and all the house of Abraham, . . . they wept exceedingly."

Death could be commonplace or majestic. It could be tragic or violent, an awesome thing to behold. But for an old man such as Abraham it could be as welcome, as simple, as inevitable, as the passing of the solstice and as natural as the ultimate dissolution of a gnarled old olive tree.

What did Death mean to Abraham?

To Isaac, man of the field, lover of Nature's bounty, earthy, plodding, dull, when his long life was over, it would come as a catalyst by which his tired body, worn and blind, would yield to Earth's warm embrace. But to Abraham, idealist, man of vision, whose unfailing faith and guidance had already led the march of feet and the march of thought for three generations of his people, and whose life was destined to influence countless more generations in the centuries to come, Death must be more than that. Perhaps, in the stillness of Canaan's heights, Death could have been for Abraham just *one step more up the mountain.*

Isaac was scarcely prepared for such outbursts of mourning as followed his father's death, nor was he unmoved by their implications. For Abraham had also been "father" to the several hundred men, women, and children who comprised his greater "family."

He stood beside his father's bier, remembering many things. For the moment, Isaac was not thinking of the great crises of Abraham's life, as he might well have been, nor of the responsibilities that now surrounded him, as Abraham's heir: he had already assumed many of his father's obligations. He was remembering instead a story from his childhood. He was hearing again the very tones of his father's voice, the patience, the pride, the happiness, they expressed.

"What did the Lord say to me?" Abraham was repeating. "The Lord said, 'I will bless you and give you a son from Sarah; and I will bless him and he shall become a people, and kings and nations shall descend from him.'"

"What is a people?" Isaac had interrupted to ask. A people is many things, as Abraham well knew, but he summed it up by saying, "To be a people, my son, is endlessly *to build together,* with tolerance, for a name's sake."

Isaac scarcely understood. "Go on, Father, go on with the story," he said.

"Then I rejoiced and said in my heart: 'Shall there be born a son to an old man, and shall Sarah, an old woman, bear a son?'" Abraham continued.

". . . Forgetting . . ." the boy prompted. Then Abraham had smiled and said, ". . . forgetting to ask myself, 'Is anything impossible to the Lord?'

"And the Lord said, 'Yea, and Sarah shall bear you a son and you shall call his name Isaac, and I will establish my everlasting covenant with him and with his children after him.'"

It was at the time of the first harvest, Isaac had been told, when the barley was ripe and the lentils hung green upon the vines, that he, Isaac, the son Abraham had longed for, for so many years, had been born to Sarah. How proud of him Abraham had always seemed to be!

Now, Isaac recalled Abraham's gifts to his other sons, Ishmael and the six sons of Keturah, and remembered how his father had sent the other sons away and designated him, Isaac, Sarah's son, his heir.

Standing by his father's bier, he remembered, too, many quiet talks with his father, over the years. They had begun as random questions and observations as to the mysteries of life

and death and of woodland and weather lore, and had lengthened as Isaac grew older. Now Isaac recognized them for what
they had always been: lessons in faith and leadership and law
and family obligation; and inspiration for the privilege, satisfactions, and responsibilities of being the Lord's steward and
leader of a clan which, Abraham believed, was destined to
perpetuate his "name" and "be a blessing to mankind."

It was Isaac's family now. But Abraham's "name" would
continue. And the "name" — so the early Mesopotamians had
concluded — was the life, the spirit, of all that a man stood for.

The mystery of that elusive something — an eternal existence
— that men in every country had forever struggled to discover,
would persist. The Sumerian seal, the Canaanite stela, the
Egyptian obelisk, and the poor man's shard, all had sought
to capture and hold immortality. Primitive men in "the river
country" had put life, spirit, into their tools and treasures with
the "word" with which they named each one. The childless
Canaanite had left his "name," his "word," on the rock in the
wilderness or his "mark" on a broken shard. *Always the desire
to "leave one's mark" upon the world!* Mesopotamians, searching for the fruit of the tree of life; Gilgamesh, legendary king
of Erech, hunting the world over to find and question Ziusudra,
the only mortal he had ever heard of who was said to have
achieved immortality! The monthly moon, rising reborn, in
"the river country"; the drama of Creation, re-enacted each
morning when the sun "rose again" in Egypt; the poor man's
shard, the rich man's tomb! *Always the age-old longing for
assurance of everlasting life!*

Abraham's journeys had been migrations of thought as
well as peoples; and, with his death, memories of his wise and
patient leadership lived on. For nearly forty centuries, his
name has been the synonym of faith. The stories he brought
from Mesopotamia have become the legends of his people.
Three great religions now acclaim him. To Christians, Jews,
and Moslems around the world, he is the great leader of the
faithful, the "Father" of his people, the "Friend of God." Abraham was dead, but his "name" was secure.

Together, his sons Ishmael and Isaac buried Abraham beside Sarah, the beloved wife, in the cave of Machpelah which, many years before, Abraham had bought from Ephron the Hittite for a family sepulchre. For Abraham, the pilgrimage was complete and his search for the Lord's favor was over. In the mountains of Canaan he had found the Lord Most High, *el-Shaddai*. Not in the stela, the obelisk, the seal, or the shard, but in his sons and grandsons, his "name" lived on. From Ishmael would stem the Arab nation, from Jacob (Israel) would come the long line of the Children of Israel. In his children, Abraham had found immortality.

> O, God Most High, *el-Shaddai*,
> Happy is that people whose God is the Lord.

Notes

General Comments

Most of the narrative chapters of this book are based upon the Biblical stories of Abraham as found in Genesis 11:26-31; and 12:1 to 25:11. Another ancient Hebrew document, listed among the Apocryphal books of the Bible, the *Book of Jubilees* or *Little Genesis*, has also been used, with discretion.

These legends are presented against a factual background based upon our present knowledge and understanding of geography, history, archaeology, and critical Biblical scholarship, as suggested in the Bibliography and by the sources and references listed in these Notes.

The Book of Genesis is a combination of three major earlier documents. designated as *J, E,* and *P*. *J* is thought to have been written *c*. 850 B.C.E.; *E, c*. 750 B.C.E.; and the two combined *c*. 650 B.C.E. P is called the priestly document and was probably not introduced into Genesis until *c*. 400 B.C.E.

It is in the *P* sections of Genesis that the genealogies and various statements regarding Abraham's age are found. Since there seem to be sound reasons for regarding these figures as unreliable (and since archaeologists have discovered equally fantastic figures regarding the ages of the kings of Sumer and Mesopotamia, and the length of their reigns), they have not been used in our story.

The *Book of Jubilees* or *Little Genesis* is an ancient Hebrew document long believed to have been written in the latter part of the second century B.C.E. Dr. William F. Albright, however, now places it in the early third (or even late fourth) century B.C.E. (Albright, *From the Stone Age to Christianity*, 2nd edition; p. 266f). It is called the *Little Genesis* because it purports to be a series of revelations made by an angel to Moses, giving him in forty-nine separate revelations the divine interpretation of mankind's history, beginning with Creation and ending with the giving of the law on Sinai. The fifty-year climax, coming at the end of seven cycles of seven, provides the name, the *Book of Jubilees*. Much in this ancient document seems fantastic to modern thought, yet, since the book contains certain vivid and intimate human touches, parts of it have been introduced into this book.

The Biblical myths of *Creation* and *The Flood* and reference to the story of *The Tower of Babel* have also been included, because it is now quite generally believed by Biblical scholars that these myths arose in the Mesopotamian valley among the people with whom Abraham's forebears lived. They were among the common traditions carried by Abraham's people into Canaan, where the Hebrews later revised them, giving them a monotheistic unity.

Except when stated otherwise, Biblical quotations are from the King James version.

The symbol B.C. is replaced by B.C.E. (Beginning of the Common Era), a term acceptable to both Jewish and Christian scholars.

Chapter 1
"Before Abraham Was . . ."

1. Childe, *Man Makes Himself*, chap. VI and VII. Frankfort, *Before Philosophy*, chap. I. Albright, *From Stone Age to Christianity*, 2nd ed., chap. III.
2. Frankfort, *op. cit.*, pp. 142-148.
3. Albright, *op. cit.*, p. 99.

200

Chapter 2
The Amazing Sumerians

4. Coon, *The Story of Man,* pp. 240 f.
5. Childe, *Man Makes Himself,* pp. 93 f.
6. *Ibid,* pp. 143 ff. A full chapter on the development of writing.
7. Albright, *From Stone Age to Christianity,* 2nd ed., p. 9.
8. Child, *op. cit.,* p. 180.

Chapter 3
Who Created the World?

The Biblical Source: Genesis 1.
9. Frankfort, *Before Philosophy,* p. 194. Finegan, *Light from the Ancient Past,* pp. 50-54.
10. King, *The Seven Tablets of Creation,* vol. I.
11. American Standard Revised Version of Genesis 1.

Chapter 4
The Great Flood — in Legend and in Fact

The Biblical Source: Genesis 6-9.
12. Woolley, *Ur of the Chaldees,* pp. 26 f.
13. *Ibid.,* chap. I. Woolley, *Excavations at Ur,* chap. I.
14. Woolley, *The Sumerians,* p. 21.
15. Frankfort, *Before Philosophy,* pp. 226 f.
16. Pritchard, *Ancient Near Eastern Texts,* pp. 42-44. Finegan, *Light from the Ancient Past,* pp. 23-30. Kramer, *Sumerian Mythology.*
17. Genesis 6:5-9:17.
18. Albright, *From Stone Age to Christianity,* 2nd ed., p. 128.

Chapter 5
Honors for the Lady Shub-ad

19. Woolley, *The Sumerians,* pp. 21 ff.
20. Childe, *Man Makes Himself,* pp. 180, 184.
21. Woolley, *Excavations at Ur,* chap. III, "The Royal Cemetery" (1954). Woolley, *Ur Excavations: The Royal Cemetery* (1934). Woolley, *Ur of the Chaldees,* chap. I, II.
22. Dr. Woolley tells of a lady buried in one of the other "royal tombs" who, not having found time perhaps to put her hair ribbon in place like her companions, had brought it, rolled up, in her pocket. It was found beside her, after nearly forty-five hundred years, rolled into a little spiral blob (Woolley, *Ur of the Chaldees,* pp. 62 f.) and is on display at the Museum of the University of Pennsylvania, Philadelphia. The same museum offers a superb collection of articles from Mesopotamia and Sumer and from the "royal tombs" of Ur.

Chapter 6
Abraham and the Images

The Biblical Source: Genesis 11:27, 28. In Joshua 24:2, Joshua, addressing all the clans of Israel, said: *Your fathers dwelt on the other side of the flood [Mesopotamia] in old time, even Terah, the father of Abraham and the father of Nahor: and they served other gods.* Apparently it had long been accepted in Joshua's time that Abraham and his family originally lived in the Mesopotamian valley and that he and his people worshiped the gods of that country.

23. The author's imaginative reconstruction of life in the city of Ur (chapters 5 through 9) is dependent upon the writings of Sir Leonard Woolley, who led the joint expeditions of the British Museum of London and the Museum of the University of Pennsylvania in excavating the city. In particular I would name the following, three of which are paper-covered books inexpensively available to the student. Others are listed in the Selected Bibliography. *Abraham: Recent Discoveries and Hebrew Origins* (Charles Scribner's Sons, 1937); *Ur of the Chaldees* (Pelican Books, 1950); *Ur: the First Phases* (Penguin Books Ltd., 1946); *The Sumerians* (Oxford, Clarendon Press, 1928); *Digging Up the Past* (Pelican Books, 1949).

24. It was Ur-nammu who, while serving as governor of Ur under the last king of Erech, overthrew "the kingship" of Erech and founded the First Dynasty of Ur with himself as king.

25. Woolley, *Ur of the Chaldees*, pp. 145 f.

26. *Ibid.*, pp. 158 f.

27. *Ibid.*, pp. 164-169.
    For further description of houses in ancient Ur, see Woolley, *Excavations at Ur,* chap. VII; Woolley, *The Sumerians,* pp. 156-160; and Woolley, *Abraham,* chap. III.

28. See *General Comments* at the beginning of Notes for description and date of the *Book of Jubilees.*

29. *Book of Jubilees,* XII:13-17; Schodde translation.

Chapter 7
THE ZIGGURAT OF UR

30. Woolley, *Ur of the Chaldees,* p. 122. Woolley, *The Sumerians,* pp. 140-155.

31. For further description of the ziggurat see also Woolley, *Excavations at Ur,* pp. 122-240.

Chapter 8
TWILIGHT AND DAWN

32. For many phases of life in Ur in the time of Abraham see Woolley, *Abraham.*

33. *Book of Jubilees,* XII:13-15.

Chapter 9
FAREWELL TO UR, FAREWELL TO SUMER

The Biblical Source: Genesis 11:27-32.

34. Scholars are fairly well agreed that Abraham's family probably moved to Harran during the troubled period of the Elamite and Amorite invasions. Dr. Jack Finegan offers a date of around 1935 B.C.E. "Surely it was a likely time for a family to depart from its old home." Finegan, *Light from the Ancient Past,* p. 60.

35. Woolley, *Abraham,* chap. 3.

36. *Ibid.*, pp. 101-104.

37. Woolley, *Abraham,* pp. 104-107. Woolley, *Excavations at Ur,* pp. 190-194.

38. According to the latest *World Almanac* (1956), these are the figures for the three religious groups referred to: Christians (Roman Catholic, Eastern Orthodox, and Protestant): 799,908,066; Jews: 11,627,450; Moslems: 321,931,336.

39. At the time Genesis was written, the country of Sumer was called *Chaldea,* taking its name from a Semitic people who invaded southern

Babylonia some time "around 1000 B.C.E. as far as we can tell" and eventually established the Chaldean empire. Finegan, *Light from the Ancient Past,* p. 57.

40. Albright, *From Stone Age to Christianity,* 2nd ed., pp. 179 f.
41. The Hurrians, a people unknown to scholars until a few decades ago, settled in northern Mesopotamia and the east-Tigris country in the third millennium and, in the second millennium, as archaeology now discovers, played an extremely important role in the cultural history of the entire Middle East from the Tigris to the Mediterranean. Albright, *op. cit.,* pp. 109 f.
42. Genesis 11:31, 32b.

Chapter 10
ABRAHAM'S "PEOPLE"

The Biblical Source: Genesis 11:32; 12:1-5a.

43. Frazer, *The Golden Bough,* vol. V, p. 303.
44. *Book of Jubilees,* Schodde translation, XII:17-21a.
45. Genesis 12:1-4.
46. Genesis 12:5a.

Chapter 13
MOUNT OF THE AMORITE

47. For the geography of Canaan, see *The Westminster Historical Atlas of the Bible.*
48. In the light of such recent archaeological evidence as the following, we must discard the old idea which pictured ancient Canaan as a backward country. "The cultural climax of this millennium [3000 to about 2100 B.C.] was in its second quarter, as illustrated by the extensive ruins of the city of Beth-yerah ('House of the Moon') at the southern end of the Sea of Galilee. . . ." Albright, *op. cit.,* p. 119. "The period between 3500 and 2500 B.C. was one of great prosperity for the country. Among the cities then in existence was . . . *Khirbet-Kerak*" (another name for Beth-yerah, *Westminster Atlas,* p. 108b). This city "is a good illustration of the prosperity of the period, for it is a huge site, covering nearly sixty acres." *Westminster Atlas,* p. 106b.

Chapter 14
CANAAN

49. Albright, *From Stone Age to Christianity,* 2nd ed., pp. 175-178. Albright, *Archaeology and the Religion of Israel,* chap. III.
50. Albright, *From Stone Age to Christianity,* 2nd ed., p. 12.
51. *Ibid.,* pp. 109 f.
52. Finegan, *Light from the Ancient Past,* p. 46.
53. *Ibid.,* pp. 54 f.

Chapter 15
THE "HIGH PLACE" OF SHECHEM

The Biblical Source: Genesis 12:6-9.

54. Albright, *op. cit.,* p. 176.
55. Genesis 12:7b.
56. This settlement was called *Luz* until Jacob, Abraham's grandson, renamed it Beth-el (meaning "home of the god"), the name by which it is commonly known.
57. The settlement called *Ai* was already a ruin in Abraham's time: in fact, the word Ai means "ruin."
58. *Book of Jubilees,* Schodde translation, XIII:5-9.

Chapter 16
THREAT OF FAMINE
The Biblical Source: Genesis, 12:10.
59. Gurney, *The Hittites,* pp. 184 ff.
60. Genesis 12:10.

Chapter 17
EGYPTIAN INTERLUDE
The Biblical Source: Genesis 12:11-20; 13:1, 2.
61. Genesis 12:11-20; 13:1, 2.
62. Pfeiffer, *Introduction to the Old Testament,* p. 283.
63. Breasted, *A History of Egypt,* Chapter X; for religious and social aspects of Egyptian life at this time, see also Breasted, *Development of Religion and Thought in Ancient Egypt.*
64. Frankfort, *Before Philosophy,* pp. 118 f.
65. *Ibid.,* pp. 240 f.
66. *Time* magazine, Nov. 19, 1956. For further description of the finding and identification of the scrolls, see also Davies, A. Powell, *The Meaning of the Dead Sea Scrolls,* p. 12; Burrows, Millar, *The Dead Sea Scrolls,* pp. 1-70; *Time* magazine, Feb. 20, 1956; and *The New York Times,* Nov. 9, 1956.

Chapter 18
LOT'S CHOICE
The Biblical Source: Genesis 13.
67. Genesis 13:8-10.
68. Burrows, *What Mean These Stones?,* p. 199; also p. 71.
69. Genesis 13:13.
70. Genesis 13:14-17.
71. Genesis 13:18.

Chapter 19
THE BATTLE OF THE KINGS
The Biblical Source: Genesis 14.
72. Burrows, *What Mean These Stones?,* p. 71.

Chapter 20
A SON FOR ABRAHAM
The Biblical Source: Genesis 15, 16.
73. Genesis 15:8.
74. Genesis 15:18.
75. Genesis 16:7-11; 16:15.

Chapter 21
ABRAHAM AND ISHMAEL AND THE HULUPPU TREE
76. This story is based on *"Gilgamesh and the Huluppu Tree: A Reconstructed Sumerian Text* (at least 2000 B.C.) translated by Samuel N. Kramer, Oriental Institute of Chicago Assyriological Studies, No. 10; University of Chicago Press, April, 1938." It is used with Dr. Kramer's permission.

Chapter 22
"A SIGN UPON HIM THAT HE IS THE LORD'S"
The Biblical Source: Genesis 17:1-14; 17:22-27.
77. Albright, *From the Stone Age to Christianity,* 2nd ed., p. 189.
78. *Ibid.,* p. 188; also p. 326, N. 63; and *Westminster Historical Atlas,* p. 26b.
79. *Book of Jubilees,* Schodde translation, XV:18.

Chapter 23
The Lord's Messengers

The Biblical Source: 18:1-33; 19:1-30; 21:1-8.

80. Adapted from translation of Genesis 18:1-16 given in Kent's *Beginnings of Hebrew History,* pp. 88 f.
81. Adapted from Genesis 18:17-33.
82. Genesis 19:23-26.
83. The Sumerian story of the *Tower of Babel* can be found in Andre Parrot's *The Tower of Babel;* the Biblical version in Genesis 11:1-9.
84. *Westminster Historical Atlas,* pp. 26a, 66a.

Chapter 24
Hagar and Ishmael

The Biblical Source: Genesis 21:8-21a.

85. Genesis 21:14a.
86. Pritchard, *The Ancient Near East in Pictures Relating to the Old Testament,* p. 136, plate 389; and description of same, p. 295.

Chapter 25
The Sacrifice of Isaac

The Biblical Source: Genesis 22:1-20.

87. Albright, *From the Stone Age to Christianity,* 2nd ed., pp. 45, 47: "Nearly every book and passage of the Old Tetsament has been stigmatized as a literary forgery by at least one scholar. Now it cannot be emphasized too strongly that there is hardly any evidence at all in the ancient Near East for documentary or literary fabrications. . . . As critical study of the Bible is more and more influenced by the rich new material from the ancient Near East we shall see a steady rise in respect for the historical significance of now neglected or despised passages and details in the Old and New Testaments."
88. Pfeiffer, *Introduction to the Old Testament,* p. 331.
89. Genesis 22:1-3a.
90. Genesis 22:9-18.

Chapter 26
The Silver Boat Sails

The Biblical Source: Genesis 23.

91. *Great Mountain* was an early Semitic term for God. Albright, *From the Stone Age to Christianity,* 2nd ed., p. 186.
92. This prayer is a composite using the phraseology of ancient psalms, of which Ps. 88 is the oldest.
93. Genesis 23:17-19.

Chapter 27
A Wife for Isaac

The Biblical Source: Genesis 24.

94. Compare with descriptions of Bedouin life and peoples in Doughty's *Arabia Deserta.*

Chapter 29
Fulfillment

The Biblical Source: Genesis 25:8-11.

95. According to Genesis 25:7, Abraham lived to be 175 years old. Scholars do not take this figure seriously, as explained in the *General Comments* at the beginning of these Notes.
96. The vivid and moving details of this scene have been taken from the *Book of Jubilees,* Schodde translation, XXII:1 to XXIII:6.

Selected Bibliography

I. General Early Background

Albright, William F., *From the Stone Age to Christianity*, 2nd ed. Baltimore: Johns Hopkins Press, 1940.

Childe, V. Gordon, *Man Makes Himself*. New York: A Mentor Book (M. 64), 1951. First published in 1941 by Watts and Co., London.

———, *What Happened in History*. London: Penguin Books, 1942.

Coon, Carleton S., *The Story of Man*. New York: Alfred A. Knopf, 1954.

Finegan, Jack, *Light from the Ancient Past*. Princeton: Princeton University Press, 1946.

Frankfort, Henri, ed., *Before Philosophy*. Pelican Books (No. A 198), 1954. First published in 1946 by University of Chicago Press under the title, *The Intellectual Adventure of Ancient Man*.

Lods, Adolphe, *Israel from its Beginnings to the Middle of the Eighth Century*. New York: Alfred A. Knopf, 1932. Introductory chapters.

II. Mesopotamia and Sumer

Albright, William F., *From Stone Age to Christianity*, 2nd ed. Baltimore: Johns Hopkins Press, 1940.

Chiera, Edward, *They Wrote on Clay*. Chicago: University of Chicago Press, 1938.

King, Leonard W., ed., *The Seven Tablets of Creation or the Babylonian and Assyrian Legends concerning the Creation of the World and of Mankind*, vol. I. London: Luzac and Co., 1902.

Kramer, Samuel N., *Gilgamesh and the Huluppu Tree: A Reconstructed Sumerian Text*. Chicago: Oriental Institute of Chicago Assyriological Studies, No. 10; University of Chicago Press, April, 1938.

———, *Sumerian Mythology*. Philadelphia: American Philosophical Society, 1944.

———, *From the Tablets of Sumer*. Indian Hills, Col.: The Falcon's Wing Press, 1956.

Parrot, Andre, *Discovering Buried Worlds*, trans. by Edwin Hudson. New York: Philosophical Library, 1955.

———, *The Flood and Noah's Ark*, trans. by Edwin Hudson. (Studies in Biblical Archaeology, No. 1.) New York: Philosophical Library, 1955.

———, *The Tower of Babel*. (Studies in Biblical Archaeology, No. 2.) New York: Philosophical Library, 1955.

Pritchard, James B., *The Ancient Near East in Pictures Relating to the Old Testament*. Princeton: Princeton University Press, 1954.

———, *Ancient Near Eastern Texts Relating to the Old Testament*. Princeton: Princeton University Press, 1955.

Speiser, Ephraim A., "Mesopotamia: Light That Did Not Fail," reprinted from the *National Geographic Magazine* in *Everyday Life in Ancient Times*. Washington: National Geographic Society, 1951.

———, *Mesopotamian Origins*. Philadelphia: University of Pennsylvania Press. Also London: Oxford University Press, 1930.

Woolley, Sir Leonard, *Abraham, Recent Discoveries and Hebrew Origins.* New York: Charles Scribner's Sons, 1936.
———, *Digging Up the Past.* Pelican Books (No. A 4), 1937.
———, *Excavations at Ur: A Record of Twelve Years' Work.* London: Ernest Benn, Ltd., 1954. Also New York: Crowell Publishing Co.
———, *The Sumerians.* New York: Oxford, Clarendon Press, 1928.
———, *Ur of the Chaldees.* New York: Charles Scribner's Sons, 1930.
———, *Ur: The First Phases.* King Penguin Books, 1946.

III. The People and Religions of Canaan

Albright, *Archaeology and Religion of Israel.* Chapter III, "The Religion of the Canaanites." Baltimore: Johns Hopkins Press, 1953.
Burrows, Millar, *What Mean These Stones?* New Haven, Conn.: American Schools of Oriental Research, 1941.
Ferm, Vergilius, *Forgotten Religions.* Chapter VII, "The Religion of the Canaanites." New York: Philosophical Library, 1930.
Glueck, Nelson, "The Age of Abraham in the Negeb," *The Biblical Archaeologist,* February 1955.
Kraeling, Emil, *The Bible Atlas.* Chicago: Rand McNally and Co., 1957.
Lods, Adolphe, *op. cit.*
McCown, C. C., *The Ladder of Progress in Palestine.* New York: Harper and Brothers, 1943.
Schaeffer, Claude F. A., *The Cuneiform Texts of Ras Shamra — Ugarit.* London: Oxford University Press, 1939.
Smith, George Adam, *The Historical Geography of the Holy Land.* London: Hodder and Stoughton, 1894. Also later editions, New York.

IV. Egypt in the Twelfth Dynasty

Albright, William F., *From the Stone Age to Christianity.* 2nd ed. Baltimore: Johns Hopkins Press, 1940.
Breasted, James H., *A History of Egypt.* New York: Charles Scribner's Sons, 1905.
———, *Ancient Records of Egypt.* Vol. 1. Chicago: University of Chicago Press, 1906.
———, *Development of Religion and Thought in Ancient Egypt.* New York: Charles Scribner's Sons, 1912.
Frankfort, Henri, *op. cit.*
Hayes, William C., "Daily Life in Ancient Egypt," reprinted from the *National Geographic Magazine* in *Everyday Life in Ancient Times.* Washington: National Geographic Society, 1951.
Pritchard, James B., *Ancient Near Eastern Texts Relating to the Old Testament.* 2nd ed. Portions regarding Egypt. Princeton: Princeton University Press, 1955.
———, *Ancient Near East in Pictures Relating to the Old Testament.* Pictures regarding Egypt. Princeton: Princeton University Press, 1954.

V. Commentaries of the Biblical Record of Abraham

Albright, William F., *The Biblical Period.* Reprinted by Oxford University Press, 1952, from *The Jews: Their History, Culture and Religion,* edited by Louis Finkelstein. New York: Harper and Brothers, 1949.

————, "Old Testament World," *Interpreter's Bible,* vol. 1. Nashville: Abingdon-Cokesbury Press, 1952.

————, *Archaeology and the Religion of Israel.* Baltimore: Johns Hopkins Press, 1953.

Charles, R. H., trans., *The Book of Jubilees or Little Genesis.* London: Adam and Charles Black, 1902.

Kent, Charles F., *The Beginnings of Hebrew History.* New York: Charles Scribner's Sons, 1908.

The New Standard Bible Dictionary. 3rd ed. New York: Funk and Wagnalls, 1936.

Pfeiffer, Robert H., *Introduction to the Old Testament.* New York: Harper and Brothers, 1941.

Schodde, George H., trans., *The Book of Jubilees or Little Genesis.* Oberlin, Ohio, 1888, and New York: Macmillan Co., 1917.

Wright, G. Ernest, *Biblical Archaeology.* Philadelphia: The Westminster Press, 1957.

Wright, G. Ernest and Filson, Floyd V., editors, *Westminster Historical Atlas of the Bible.* Philadelphia: The Westminster Press, 1945.

VI.   Miscellaneous Reading

Burrows, Millar, *The Dead Sea Scrolls.* New York: The Viking Press, 1955.

Ceram, C. W., *Gods, Graves and Scholars.* (Chapters 19, 20, 21.) New York: Alfred A. Knopf, 1951.

Davies, A. Powell, *The Meaning of the Dead Sea Scrolls.* New York: New American Library.

Doughty, Charles M., *Travels in Arabia Deserta.* New York: Random House, 1921 edition, with an Introduction by T. E. Lawrence.

Frazer, Sir James G., *The Golden Bough.* New York: Macmillan Co., 1922. Also later editions.

Gurney, O. R., *The Hittites.* Pelican Books (No. A 259), 1952.

Keller, Werner, *The Bible as History.* New York: William Morrow, 1956.